The Way I See It

The Way I See It

Health Readings from the Man with
X-Ray Vision

ನ೮

JAY CALIENDO
MEDICAL INTUITIVE

EDITED BY PAMELA L. SWEARINGEN
MEDICAL WRITER

14317-CALI

To order additional copies of this book, contact:
Xlibris Corporation
1-888-7-XLIBRIS
www.Xlibris.com
Orders@Xlibris.com

Contents

FOREWORD

Jay Caliendo's gift of sight into the human body impresses me as much today as it did when we were first introduced in 1999 at a clinic here in Phoenix. He read for one of my patients at that time, and his reading was 100% accurate. Even with his accuracy I was quite skeptical at first, but the more I have worked with Jay, the more I have come to respect and rely on his abilities.

Although I was trained in allopathic (traditional) medicine and am board certified in neonatology, family medicine, and pediatrics, I have also become licensed in homeopathy and certified in acupuncture. In 2000 I submitted three of Jay's readings, which were corroborated by diagnostic studies, to *Alternative and Complementary Therapies,* the official journal of the Society of Integrative Medicine. This was the first time case studies by a medical intuitive were ever published by a medical journal.

When allopathic tests do not provide an answer for an individual with physical problems, the source is usually an energy abnormality, and Jay is able to visualize that. For example, Jay sees energy flowing through the body's meridians—the same points or channels in which we perform acupuncture. When an individual has an energy block—and Jay can detect this as well—a practitioner of energy work can get the energy flowing again. However, most allopathic physicians do not have the foundation for interpreting Jay's energy findings or treating those abnormalities. This is why individuals who have not found relief through traditional medicine may find solutions to their problems through energy work.

Jay sees the truth in an illness—the physical problems, emotional disorders, and energy blocks. By suggesting various energy practitioners, medical specialists, and other health care providers for a variety of conditions, his book of reference will open the door to the healing sought by so many.

Abraham C. Kuruvilla, MD, MD(H)
Phoenix, Arizona

PREFACE

Editor: Jay, where were you born and raised?

Jay Caliendo: I was born in Dallas, Texas in 1951. In 1959 my family moved to Phoenix, Arizona, where I still live today.

Ed: Are you married, and do you have children?

JC: I have two terrific grown children, Kimberly and John, from my first marriage. In March of 2001 I married my wonderful wife Lina, and we are raising her two sons from a previous marriage, Rendy and Reza.

Ed: Have you always been a medical intuitive?

JC: (Laughing) No, the first 22 years of my life were pretty normal. I was focused on weightlifting. The year before my medical intuition manifested, I was ranked in the top 25 of the world's strongest men for my weight class in the bench press. Later I developed my own business involving racquetball and weight training. Twenty years ago I became a police officer and was subsequently promoted to Sergeant with the Phoenix Police Department.

Ed: When did you become aware of your intuitive abilities?

JC: In 1973 when I was attending Northern Arizona University in Flagstaff I felt a void in my life, so I decided to pursue God more than an education and I became a Christian. Shortly after my public baptism I had the ability to see health-related issues in others simply by looking at them.

Ed: This must have been shocking to you. What did you think when it happened?

JC: At first I thought it was a function of coming into manhood–that I was seeing what other adults see–but I quickly learned that it was something only I was experiencing.

Ed: How do you explain being given this ability that so few people have?

JC: It is, without a doubt, a gift from God, but it confused me because I couldn't understand why God gave it to me, and I really couldn't comprehend what I was supposed to do with it.

Ed: Did you become a medical intuitive immediately after you discovered this sight?

JC: Yes, because from that moment on it has always been there and required no special effort on my part. However, for the first several years I had to work at interpreting the data I was seeing. For example, today I can distinguish malignant tumors from benign tumors or scar tissue from energy blockage. In the beginning, however, it was more difficult.

Ed: Were you ever tempted to use this gift of insight other than for reading people's health?

JC: At first I wasn't sure what to do with it and I experimented like a kid in a toy store. I read people, and my love for animals prompted me to read them too. I tried my hand at solving crimes, and I described people's homes to them—homes I had never seen. But my level of accuracy was always highest—89%—when I read people's health, and I saw that as a sign that this was to be my focus.

Ed: So you used your level of accuracy as a sign from God?

JC: Yes, and I made a promise to God that if He would continue to help me with my accuracy, I would continue to do this work no matter where it takes me. I see it as a partnership: I do what I believe He asks me to do, and He continues to show me the way.

Ed: I understand you read several hundred people a year. Have you always read that many?

JC: No. At first readings were slow to come because I didn't seek them (remember, I was only 22 years old when I was given this gift), but I prayed that if I was to do the work God would provide the people. In 1995 He answered my prayer when I was invited to work at a physical therapy clinic where I read mentally and physically disabled children. We had such positive success that the staff encouraged me to offer my readings to the public. It was the first time I had been asked to do readings for complete strangers. It has not slowed down since.

Ed: Did you volunteer at the clinic on your days off from the police department?

JC: Yes. Reading those children brought balance to my life. I couldn't wait for the week to end so I could return to the clinic and read more children.

Ed: Were you open with your fellow officers about your intuitive ability?

JC: No, not at first. I had a lot of mental struggle with it. After all, in police work there is no room for the unknown or unexplainable–by necessity–so I thought they might ridicule me. Later when I formed my corporation, Inner Insight Ltd., I was surprised that so many of them seemed to accept this gift so well. In fact, I have read my share of police officers and their families, although I do get the occasional jab.

Ed: What was your purpose in forming Inner Insight Ltd.?

JC: My objective has always been to help as many people as I can. It lead me to radio, where I took calls on health-related issues once a week, and I've also held seminars where I read everyone in the room. That was tiring but fun. Eventually I was invited to appear on local TV and national radio shows, which expanded my audience into other states and even into other countries.

Ed: Have you had any medical training?

JC: None, although I would have loved being a doctor, and I admire them greatly. I describe what I do like this: Let's say there are doctors looking at you from the front and I am looking at you from behind. We're all trying to figure out what is wrong, but I see it from a different angle. Sometimes bringing a different perspective to the table can make all the difference in helping an individual get well.

Ed: How easy is it for you to read someone?

JC: It is very easy, like flipping through the pages of a book. I access the information I need, usually in a matter of seconds. I do what I describe as a spiritual/energy reading. This energy moves freely within the spirit, with the spirit carrying the body's information, its biography. The spirit is like the shell of an egg and the energy is like the yolk moving within. *

*Greater detail about how Jay sees energy is found in the glossary.

Ed: Do people have to be in your presence in order for you to read their health issues?

JC: No, in fact most of my readings are conducted by phone. I read people's energy, not their flesh, so distance is not relevant in my work.

Ed: Do you consider yourself part of the psychic, alternative, or traditional world?

JC: I consider myself to be mainstream. I don't promote one method over another. If I see that traditional medicine would work better than an alternative route, I say so, and vice versa.

Ed: After studying so many of your readings, it becomes clear that people do not acquire diseases in the same way, nor do you suggest the same treatments for everyone with the same illness.

JC: That's true. With fibromyalgia, for example, there is no one-size-fits-all approach to treatment that would help everyone with that diagnosis. But there are treatments I recommend in the book that likely would help people whose symptoms have not been alleviated by traditional and alternative approaches. That is why I am so excited about this book. It is one of the avenues I have for reaching people with my work. I cannot live long enough to read all the people who want me to read for them, and it is my dream that people who read this book can find an answer not only for their own health problems, but for those of their children, spouses, and friends as well.

ACKNOWLEDGMENTS

This book was written with the encouragement of many, but because of space limitations, I can acknowledge only a few:

Pamela Swearingen, for believing in the importance of this book and convincing me to write it.

Dr. Abraham Kuruvilla, MD, for his endless support and confidence in my work.

Dr. Kiera Lane, ND, for her help with the glossary definitions.

Dean Johnson, my closest friend, who always listens to me when things get difficult and tiring.

My father Ed and my mother Peg, my biggest fans. Thanks Dad for the book's title. Thank you Mom for your continued encouragement to offer my God-given gift to others.

My daughter Kimberly, for answering phones and responding to all the requests for readings during the busiest of times. I could not have managed the work without you.

My son John, who helped me go public with my intuitive work, I will always remember your encouragement and support and the contributions you have made to my work. You are a terrific son.

And to my wife, my soul mate Lina, who throughout these incredibly busy times has been such help in supporting my work and reminding me of its importance. You are my forever love.

NOTE TO THE READER

This book is alphabetized and organized according to symptoms and illnesses. Occasionally a reading may appear under more than one heading when that reading addresses a variety of symptoms. A glossary precedes the readings. I hope that referring to it will help you better understand the remedies that I recommend.

I am a medical/health intuitive. I have no medical training, and my opinions are based solely on my intuitive ability. The readings in this book reveal causes and suggest remedies for a variety of symptoms and illnesses and are meant to be used collaboratively with recommendations from your health care provider. Sometimes my visions fall in line with traditional medicine and at other times alternative medicine. Occasionally they may make no sense to any medical discipline—they are presented as I see them.

If you prefer a more conventional approach, I encourage you to seek that path. On the other hand, if you are looking for answers you have not been able to find through other avenues, I hope you will find this book informative and helpful in your quest.

Sincerely

Jay Caliendo
Website: *www.medicalintuitive.com*
e-mail: *j@medicalintuitive.com*
Voice mail: 623-465-0130

14317-CALI

GLOSSARY

Acupuncture: An ancient form of medicine that involves the insertion of fine needles into specific points in the body to stimulate the flow of energy (chi), thereby relieving pain and restoring health. Acupuncture is a component of traditional Chinese medicine.

Apple cider vinegar: A powerful detoxifying agent and immune system booster that has been used for centuries. It contains pectin, a soluble fiber that binds to cholesterol and removes it from the body; antioxidants such as beta-carotene to destroy free radicals; and a balanced mixture of vitamins, enzymes, trace elements, and minerals—particularly potassium, a known "artery detergent."

Blood-type diet: Designed by James D'Adamo, ND, and further developed by his son Peter D'Adamo, ND. This diet corresponds to the eating habits of ones ancestors. For example, people with "O," the oldest blood type comprising the largest section of the population, can eat most meats, while those with "A," the next oldest blood type, seem to do better when eating primarily fish and vegetables. Although Jay does not recommend this diet for every client, he does suggest it when he can see a positive change in the individual's health when he superimposes the diet over that person's energy flow.

Breathing, conscious: Bringing awareness to the breathing process. In normal breathing, one breathes in a cycle that starts with an inhalation (breathing oxygen into the lungs) followed by an exhalation (breathing carbon dioxide out of the lungs). Some people, however, breathe in such a shallow manner that they are not even aware that they are breathing. Breathing consciously is one way of connecting the mind with the body to improve ones health.

Breathing, diaphragmatic: Sometimes called "belly breathing" and associated with the rise and fall of the abdomen during deep breathing. This type of breathing involves the contraction and relaxation of the diaphragmatic muscle. With each breath the diaphragm contracts downward, expanding the chest cavity and forcing air into the lungs. Relaxation of the diaphragmatic muscle forces air back out. Diaphragmatic breathing increases delivery of oxygen to the body and promotes elimination of wastes.

Chiropractor (DC): Practitioner with a 4-year postgraduate degree specializing in the correction of spinal misalignment to restore the nervous system and promote health.

Detoxifying/detoxification: Involves the elimination of toxins (substances that alter the body's normal structure and function) from the body. Sources of toxins may include drugs, radiation, pesticides in foods, environmental pollutants, and chemical exposure. Detoxification entails the clearing of these toxins and wastes from the body using herbs and herbal teas, apple cider vinegar, large quantities of water, diaphragmatic breathing, laxatives, psyllium husks, enemas, colonic irrigations, traditional massage, lymphatic massage, steam baths, saunas, and exercise.

Energy: Jay talks about energy, energy flow, energy blocks, and trapped energy. When a person's energy flows normally, he sees it as an uninterrupted, oval-shaped stream from the top of the head; down the front of the body; through the groin, legs, and feet; up through the spine, back of the neck, and head; and over the front of the face and back down again. It does not leave the body; it is a continuous flow that radiates from the spirit or soul. Each person's energy is unique, like a fingerprint. Jay sees it flaring out through the body similar to a ghost's appearance, taking on the black-and-white, two-dimensional image of an x-ray film. He then converts this image into three-dimensional–like layers. He looks at it from the surface, and then continues deeper into the spiritual core, ultimately reading the entire spirit and soul. This energy reveals physical problems of the past, present, and future, and it is held by the spirit until death.

To Jay this energy has different appearances–shallow or deep, light or dark, moving or still–all representing the physical, spiritual, emotional, and psychological. Over the years he has learned to decipher and create his own guidelines, interpretations, and definitions for what he sees. By looking at energy movement or lack of it, its shading variations, and depth, he can tell whether or not the person he is reading is physically healthy, grounded, mentally stable, or happy. Viewing a person's energy gives Jay all the answers he needs, and it is the basis for his work.

Energy work/energy medicine: Restoring the body to its proper balance and circulation and strengthening the physical, emotional, and spiritual health of an individual. With Reiki, for example, energy from the practitioner enters the client's body to strengthen the physical, emotional, mental, and spiritual states. Reiki (energy from the practitioner), acupuncture, acupressure (use of hands rather than needles), massage, Rolfing, chiropractic manipulation, and reflexology are all forms of energy medicine.

Herbal (botanical) medicine: Use of plants as medicine. Plants have many powerful medicinal properties that can be used for a variety of conditions. Herbal medicine may be used in the form of pills, tea, syrup, capsules, tablets, tinctures, powders, or in its whole form.

Homeopathy: System of medicine that is over 200 years old that uses highly diluted substances called "remedies." These remedies enhance the body's own healing process using the principle "like cures like."

They may be of plant, animal, or mineral origin and are individualized for each patient.

Hypnosis/hypnotherapy: Accessing the subconscious mind to enable insight for changing behavioral patterns and thus facilitate healing of the body, mind, emotions, and spirit. The therapist commonly makes suggestions for healing while the patient is in a relaxed, hypnotic state.

Massage therapy: Applying therapeutic pressure, stroking, friction, and kneading to an area of discomfort or to the entire body using hands, forearms, fingers, or appliances. The therapist increases blood flow into blocked areas of the body to promote tissue repair and removal of toxins.

Natural hormone: Generally refers to using natural progesterone creams made of wild yams rather than the estrogens and progestins used in traditional hormone replacement therapy (HRT).

Naturopath/naturopathic physician (ND, NMD): Practitioner with a 4-year postgraduate degree from colleges of naturopathic medicine. These doctors are trained in natural medicine and use natural and non-toxic therapies such as nutritional therapy, acupuncture, herbs, detoxification, homeopathy, physical medicine, bodywork, lifestyle modification, and counseling.

Organ flushing/cleansing: Detoxifying the blood and tissues of specific organs. Methods may include fasting, juice fasting, food supplements, intestinal cleansers, herbal cleansers, apple cider vinegar, and colonic irrigations.

Osteopathic physician (DO): Practitioner with a 4-year medical school training similar to that of medical doctors but with additional training in spinal adjustment.

Psychotherapy: Using psychological modalities to bring therapeutic change in emotional, cognitive, and behavioral functioning.

Reflexology: Stimulating reflexes on the feet or hands to promote healing in other parts of the body. Reflex points on the feet and hands correspond to specific glands, organs, and other body parts.

Rolfing: Manipulating the myofascia (soft tissue) to affect changes in structure and thereby create a more efficient use of muscles and conservation of energy. Rolfing practitioners use their hands, knuckles, and elbows to separate layers of fascia in order to promote healing of injured and strained muscles.

St. John's Wort: Medicinal plant that has antiviral, antispasmodic, and antidepressant properties.

Tai Chi: Form of Chinese self-defense that coordinates fluid movements with the breath to stimulate and balance energy (chi) in the body. A strong mind-body connection is associated with this ancient art.

Yoga: Form of exercise involving aligning, strengthening, and stretching the body through specific postures and breath. Yoga benefits the physical body while promoting mind-body connection.

ACCIDENTS/TRAUMA, PROBLEMS FOLLOWING

F 50 yrs 03-27-96
Problem: She has headaches high on her forehead and over and under one eye.
Reading: The bridge of her nose and cheekbone appear to have been injured in an accident. The tendons or muscles are very tight on the front of her neck where they attach to the base of the chest. The back of her neck, three-quarters of the way down, appears to be irritated by the tight tendons. Two vertebrae between the shoulder blades are displaced. (After the reading she stated that she had been in a car accident in which her face hit the steering wheel.) She needs massage therapy and Rolfing. Her face and head need to be massaged first, and then her neck and upper back.

F 41 yrs 12-10-99
Problem: She was in a car accident in 1995, resulting in three spinal fusions in her neck. Her main concern today is her chronic diarrhea. X-ray film shows a shadow in the bile duct.
Reading: The diarrhea is linked to the bile duct and pancreatic area. Fiber in the bile duct likely was torn and bruised when she was in the car accident. This torn fiber has formed scar tissue, which is the shadow on the x-ray film. If this area can be treated, she will experience improvement with the diarrhea.

M 47 yrs 11-10-99

Problem: He was in a car accident earlier in the year. He has been treated with acupuncture, but he believes that he is not improving quickly enough.

Reading: His cranium has moved forward and down over his face. This has irritated his upper teeth and gums and lower jaw. (He then stated that his teeth and jaw have been giving him trouble). He needs acupuncture to his face in order to reduce pressure to his teeth and jaw in addition to the acupuncture he is getting to other parts of his body.

F 35 yrs 07-06-99

Problem: She hurt her back in a fall and believes it was made worse by a chiropractic treatment. She is now in extreme pain and has been lying on ice for the past month. In addition, her breasts are lactating, but she is not pregnant.

Reading: The last lumbar disk in her back has slipped forward toward the spine. A muscle fiber tear that has been bleeding is causing swelling in her lower back, which is adding to the pressure in her slipped disk. She should have acupuncture first, then perhaps reflexology. She will require 2 to 3 weeks before she will see a 75% recovery. The base of her throat is swollen, which was caused by soft tissue trauma. (She then explained that 2 months earlier she had a whiplash injury.) The pituitary gland was traumatized and is not functioning normally, which is why her breasts are lactating. This can be corrected by treating the pituitary gland with acupuncture and other energy work.

F 21 yrs 09-21-98

Problem: She suffers from a crippling disease and is currently in a wheelchair. Doctors have been unable to diagnose and help her, and she is in chronic pain.

Reading: Her condition was caused by trauma. (She then stated that she had been in three accidents several years ago, all within a period of 3 months.) She is handling it better than she thinks she is, but her main problem is that she has not accepted this illness emotionally. She needs to work on this because it is the key to her healing. Once she has fully accepted this illness as just something that has happened to her, she can then begin to attack it physically. She should see a hypnotherapist to start the emotional healing and then have some energy work done. She has an energy block that starts about 2 inches from the top of her forehead and runs straight through her body into her digestive tract. She needs to increase her vegetable intake but in a liquid form; her body likely cannot digest them in solid form. She also needs to increase her potassium intake. It would be good for her to lie flat on her back as much as possible, with her head flat on the floor. She can put something under her feet if that feels better, but the rest of her body needs to be flat. This will help open up the energy in her body, which in turn will help her digestive system. She is also prone to urinary tract infections. This is an energy problem; increasing her water intake will help.

F 57 yrs 09-28-98
Problem: She fell a month ago, hurting her head, shoulder, hip, and buttocks. She also has a ringing in her ears.
Reading: Her hips and lower back are in need of chiropractic treatment. They are not holding adjustments. The muscles are wrapping tightly around the lumbar area and pulling on the pelvis. A Rolfer needs to work on this area, initially avoiding the buttocks because of the deep bruising. Her mid-thoracic area has a nerve that flares out in both directions. After the chiropractic treatment, she should receive reflexology to help heal the lumbar and pelvic areas. The ringing in her ears is a result of the fall.

F 49 yrs 03-17-97
Problem: She was in a car accident 10 years ago and now walks with a cane. She has had a transcutaneous electrical nerve stimulator (TENS) unit implanted in the middle of her back. She wants to know what she can do for her physical and emotional pain.
Reading: She needs to forget about the accident and stop trying to figure out why it happened to her. Her health is better than she thinks it is. She needs to focus on her strengths—her mind, eyes, arms, and

hands. Working with indoor plants, sewing, meditating, and relaxing (but not too much) would be good for her. She might consider getting Rolfed. Her chest gets tight with stress when she worries about her health. The stress on her heart caused by worrying could lead to other problems.

Brighter days are ahead if she would think more positively. Her neck may need adjustment because it is causing energy blockage in the inside forearms just below the biceps. A lack of exercise will only make the pain worse. She is in control of her health, more so than the doctors. Her health can improve or get worse—it is mostly up to her.

F 55 yrs 10-12-98

Problem: She had a car accident 9 months ago and suffered back bruises and knee, shoulder, and neck injuries. Her tailbone is swollen, and she has been using oils and magnets to overcome the pain. Her eyes feel tired all the time, and she has trouble digesting her food. Before the accident she was very healthy.

Reading: The thoracic area of the spine is her main problem. A lower thoracic vertebra is most likely causing the digestive problems. Her fifth cervical vertebra is causing neck spasms, and her tired eyes are related to her neck injury. She needs energy work because there is a blockage that starts at the lower chest and then drops down through the digestive organs, contributing to the diarrhea. The tailbone is bruised and slightly tilted, and her knee problems are connected to this injury. A nerve that runs down from the top of the head causes the tenderness in the temple area. A chiropractor needs to continue with the cranial work. Her jawbone is very tight, which is emotional, not physical.

F 28 yrs 10-09-00

Problem: She is very fatigued.

Reading: She has an energy blockage shaped like a horseshoe that starts at the center of her head, runs down behind her ears, and angles forward down to the base of her neck. This shutting down of energy was caused by an injury, not by stress. (She then revealed that she fell out of a car at 2 years of age.) She needs reflexology and Rolfing for the cranial area. Her fatigue is 60% to 70% caused by the head and neck injury and subsequent energy block. Exhausted adrenal glands are responsible for the other 30% to 40%.

F 38 yrs 01-07-00

Problem: Her main concern is fibromyalgia and severe body pain, which increases with inclement weather. She is taking medication and herbs for pain and sleep problems, but she has to use them judiciously because she cares for her two young children. She has been diagnosed with lupus and has a history of several car accidents.

Reading: The car accidents are the main cause of her health problems. The lupus is not as serious as the fibromyalgia, which is well advanced. She needs emotional work, physical exercise, yoga, breathing exercises, and to do activities that are fun for her. Acupuncture would not be beneficial.

F 51 yrs 02-05-01

Problem: She fell off a three-story ladder 4 years ago. For the past 3 years she has been unable to move her arms and legs and is in a wheelchair. If she is lying down, her arms and legs relax, but if she is moved, her extremities tighten up. Four years ago a doctor diagnosed her as having multiple sclerosis (MS), although two other doctors have said that she does not have it.

Reading: Two veins in her neck were stretched leaving microtears when she fell. Her paralysis began at that time. This is not MS or a nerve injury but rather a lack of blood and oxygen supply to the extremities, which prevents the nerves from working sufficiently. She should see a doctor who also performs acupuncture and consult a physical therapist for exercises to strengthen the front part of the neck.

F 57 yrs 02-13-01

Problem: She has had leg and lower back pain since having been hit by a car 6 years ago.

Reading: She shows the appearance of a muscle tug of war, with some of her muscles and ligaments pulling her neck backward and others pulling her neck forward and down into the chest. Her occipital area is locked as well. She needs either acupuncture or Rolfing of the neck and chest. The lumbar and sacral areas would benefit from Rolfing and chiropractic treatment to relieve the leg pain. The sacrum is tilted forward and off center, causing the back pain.

M 77 yrs 02-26-01

Problem: He has had near constant headaches for 15 years since having had a car accident. He had laser surgery to the brainstem that relieved 50% of his neck pain.

Reading: The headaches, which resemble migraines, are caused by tight cranial muscles that are restricting blood flow through the veins in the back and side of his head. Acupuncture to these areas may be a viable treatment. He should also apply hot, moist heat to the back of the head to help alleviate the headaches.

F 52 yrs 03-12-01

Problem: She was in a car accident 6 years ago that resulted in left-sided head injury, memory loss, difficulty with words and addition, and the inability to continue work as an engineer. Her doctors tell her that she cannot be cured and have diagnosed her with fibromyalgia and chronic fatigue. She gets very tired and is in a lot of pain with muscle spasms.

Reading: The axis at the base of her head has moved forward, causing headaches and swallowing and breathing problems. Her brain appears to be adhering to the inside of the cranium. Rolfing or acupuncture may enable her head and brain to return to the correct anatomical position. She also needs to have a physician look into the serotonin or other chemical that appears to be leaking into her brain. This chemical is too abundant and is causing muscle soreness and stiffness, as well as contributing to the headaches.

F 58 yrs 06-10-01

Problem: For 30 years she has had sharp pain under the right ribcage that worsens in the afternoon and is somewhat relieved when she lies down. Although diagnostic tests have been negative, doctors believe that her problem may be centered in her stomach. The pain can stay for 2 days and then disappear for a week. She once had a lot of energy, but now it is greatly diminished.

Reading: The problem could be a result of a head injury or trauma to the brain–perhaps an injury to the vagus nerve or a nerve connected to the stomach or digestive tract. (She said that she had been a bull rider and suffered many head injuries and concussions.) She should have acupuncture to the vagus (or appropriate) nerve in the brain. This seems to be her primary problem.

M 57 yrs 06-30-01

Problem: He has had chronic lower back pain for 40 years. He has had three lumbar disk surgeries and wears a morphine patch to help control the pain. He wants to know why his back pain is still so severe.

Reading: He has suffered trauma to his face up under the chin or nose that forced his head back and into the brainstem, causing nerve damage to the spinal cord. This is causing his back pain. His problem is nerve disruption–not a disk problem. (He said that he had concussions from high school football, motorcycle accidents, and fistfights.) Most likely the football injury is the cause of his back pain because he has had pressure on his brainstem for a long time. He should have cranial work–Rolfing or acupuncture–to the base of his skull to move the head forward and thus relieve pressure on the nerves in the brainstem and spinal cord.

M 56 yrs 06-02-01

Problem: He fell from the roof of his house 20 years ago and has had headaches since then that can last for 5 days at a time. Whichever side of his head he sleeps on is the side in which the headache occurs. His head feels as though it is on fire, and his skull is hot to the touch. Neurologic tests have all been negative. Diet, alcohol, fans, and breezes can trigger a headache. After the injury, he had acupuncture for 6 years, which helped because he was not able to hold his head up before this treatment.

Reading: The headaches and burning in his head are caused by a lack of oxygen to the brain. Vertebrae in his upper and lower neck and thorax have affected the nerves that control the lungs. Acupuncture and other energy work help because they open blocked energy and enable optimal oxygen flow. The problem returns when he stops his treatment. For more lasting results he should have his neck, upper thorax, and lungs worked on rather than his head.

F 7 yrs 07-21-01

Problem: She has had nausea and a headache over her right eyebrow for the past year. She complains constantly about not feeling well. She has difficulty going to sleep, and it is just as difficult to wake up. She prefers not to talk or express herself. One year ago she fell out of a bunk bed and struck her face. Doctors do not believe that this accident is related to her headache.

Reading: Her problems were caused by trauma, and falling out of bed appears to be the likely event. Doctors have not found the problem because they are focusing on her head and brain while the problem centers around her neck, shoulders, and chest. The atlas at her first cervical vertebra is rotated because her head is twisted to the side and not balanced over her neck and shoulders. This is interfering with the nerves in her neck and shoulders and causing the headaches. Several pressure points and nerves in her upper chest, back, shoulders, diaphragm, and clavicle need to be treated. First she needs Rolfing to these areas and then acupuncture.

ADRENAL GLAND PROBLEMS

F 58 yrs 07-20-99
Problem: She has left side pain under the ribcage that comes across or under the breast. She belches a lot, which relieves the pain. She has had this pain for over 15 years. A naturopath is treating her with acupuncture, but she is not getting better.
Reading: She does not have stomach or colon problems. The problem stems from the adrenal gland over her left kidney. The kidney looks good, but it does have pressure on it. She has a tumor either on the adrenal gland or between the adrenal gland and the kidney. She needs blood work and other diagnostic tests of this area.

M 54 yrs 11-26-99
Problem: He has low blood pressure, stomach ulcers, and body pain. He is also taking medications for depression.
Reading: He is depleted of minerals. His kidneys are failing because his adrenal glands are depleted, and his adrenal glands are depleted because of a lack of minerals. The medication he is taking for depression is having a negative affect on his adrenal glands. He should be on a natural herb for his depression, and his urine should be tested to confirm mineral loss.

F 41 yrs 10-17-99
Problem: She has had gum and tooth inflammation for the past week and a cold for the past 3 weeks. She also has back, neck, shoulder, and lumbar discomfort. Her appetite is poor, and tests by a naturopath have revealed problems with her liver, gallbladder, kidneys, and adrenal glands.
Reading: She has an energy blockage that is 2 inches above the navel

that runs through the digestive organs, kidneys, and adrenal glands, back up through her back and base of the head, down through the back of the neck, and into the trapezius muscles. Her adrenal glands are 70% exhausted. This energy blockage is stress-related. The order of treatment should be (1) her emotions and (2) hands-on energy work to clear the blockage. The tooth and gum problem is energy-related. The prolonged cold is caused by the exhausted adrenal glands.

F 49 yrs 09-04-00

Problem: She has intense muscle burning and soreness. She began weight training a year ago, at which time her muscles began getting sore. The soreness became more intense and lasted longer as time went on. Eventually she could not even go for walks. Her muscles feel as though they are burning, particularly from the waist down. She cannot sleep because of this muscle problem. Her thyroid gland was removed 10 years ago.

Reading: The main cause of the burning muscles is her adrenal glands. Her body seems to be producing too much alkali or acid in the muscle and tissue. The tissue and muscle give the appearance of being separated from each other—not torn or tearing, but just not working in conjunction. She should see an endocrinologist to look at her adrenal hormone levels. This adrenal problem developed as a reaction to stress, which she needs to learn how to control. She could see a naturopath about adrenal supplements, and if she were to have adrenal acupuncture, she would see improvement in 2 weeks with more improvement in 2 months.

F 65 yrs 03-03-01

Problem: She has had headaches, dizziness, and chills for 2 years. Three chiropractors have been unable to tell her the cause.

Reading: Hormones from her adrenal gland are low, and she becomes dizzy when she moves quickly or gets tired. This is also the reason for her headaches and chills. The adrenal gland should be treated with acupuncture and herbs. Then after about 60 days of this treatment, her hormone levels should be checked, and if they are low, she should begin taking an adrenal hormone.

F 73 yrs 03-10-01

Problem: Her feet became paralyzed 1 year ago, but magnetic resonance imaging (MRI) and x-ray examinations are negative. She is now incontinent of urine and lacks bladder control.

Reading: Her bladder control and foot condition are caused by her adrenal glands. She needs to see an endocrinologist. Her hormone level has affected her neurologic system. She has too much salt in her system because of the adrenal problem and this is affecting her bladder.

F 34 yrs 03-19-01

Problem: She has not felt well for 10 years. She has had bloating, irritability, erratic menstrual cycles, tender and lactating breasts, premenstrual syndrome (PMS), low sex drive, pain during intercourse, swollen neck glands (recent), and anger. She has had many diagnostic tests, but so far physicians have found only that she is low in progesterone. She has been on progesterone replacement for 5 years and feels somewhat better.

Reading: Her adrenal glands have an unusual look to them–they appear to sit into the kidneys rather than on top of them. This is a cause for concern, and she should see an endocrinologist. The adrenal glands are most likely the cause of her hormone imbalance and her swollen neck glands. She also has blocked energy to the reproductive area, which along with her low sex drive, is caused by her emotional state as a result of not feeling well physically.

F 55 yrs 04-29-01

Problem: She was diagnosed with chronic fatigue 8 years ago. She began eating a lot of chocolate and then stopped consuming it and caffeine "cold turkey." In the past 6 months she has had a throbbing in her solar plexus that comes and goes. Sometimes she feels as though her blood is on fire and that she is about to go into a coma, so she has to force herself to walk around. She also has nasal polyps that interfere with her breathing but has put off surgery because she believes she is too weak right now.

Reading: Her adrenal glands are not just exhausted; they are totally inactive and are not functioning at all. This might have occurred because of a shock to her system, and her abrupt dietary change and lack of good energy flow may have had something to do with this. She needs lymphatic massage to the upper chest, extending to the breast tissue. The sensation of fire in her blood is the result of the lack of adrenal function. The base of her neck and upper back are very tight, and these areas are the key to regaining her health. Acupuncture or Rolfing to these areas will restore her lungs, adrenal glands, breasts, lymphatics, and possibly even her sinuses.

F 45 yrs 06-27-01

Problem: She has been diagnosed as clinically dead four times in her life. About 3 weeks ago she was rushed to the hospital with no pulse. The first time it happened she was 29 years of age and cycling on her bike when she passed out after her heart had stopped. Her heart beats quickly and then stops. Doctors say she has a somewhat leaky heart valve but it is not severe enough to warrant surgery. She has had treadmill tests, injections of dye, and workups by eight different heart specialists, but no one has been able to determine what causes her to "die" when her heart stops and then return to life. She had been on many heart medications and blood thinners but now is taking only beta blockers.

Reading: She has a serious adrenal gland disorder. Either they stop functioning or they cease producing hormones, which immediately affects the pituitary and reproductive glands, temporarily shutting down all body functions and sending the body into shock. She needs to see an endocrinologist. The adrenal glands should be treated with herbs, acupuncture, and reflexology to determine if this improves the pituitary and reproductive glands, as well as the heart.

F 17 yrs 07-19-01

Problem: She has had a muscle weakness problem since she was 15 months of age. She had difficulty sitting up and was slow to walk. Her knees pop out of their sockets, and unexpectedly she will have sharp muscle pain that runs down her arms, hands, and legs. This intense pain can last between 30 seconds and 3 minutes. Her muscles also twitch under her eyes and in her fingers, upper arms, and thighs. One week these symptoms can occur several times and the next week not at all. Her voice also has a fast, low pitch. One MRI has shown white lesions on her brain, but a second showed none. Doctors are stumped and have tentatively diagnosed her as having multiple sclerosis.

Reading: Thousands of white crystals form on her brain (or pass over the top of her brain) and seep into her body, disrupting the natural flow of her nervous system. These crystals have the appearance of rain falling gently, covering and then saturating her muscles before being absorbed by the cells. This is why one MRI found them and the second did not. She was born with abnormal adrenal glands—one is barely developed and the other is of a more normal size. This adrenal dysfunction is causing this unusual chemical release. She needs to see an endocrinologist. If her adrenal glands are not diseased and are, in fact, developed sufficiently, this problem may be treatable.

ALLERGIES

F 12 yrs 02-08-98

Problem: When she was younger she was allergic to most chemicals and detergents.

Reading: She is not overly allergic to much of anything. Clogged pores mostly cause these reactions, with the worst area under the arms. She needs to sweat by taking frequent saunas and drink a lot of water. She needs to get the outside of her body to breathe and the inside of her body to flush. A moist, warm cloth will help the clogged pores on her face. She could suffer from ear infections because of a buildup of wax and fluid. She needs a chiropractor to adjust her upper neck routinely to keep her ear canals open, which will help prevent ear infections.

F 59 yrs 04-10-98
Problem: Her hair lacks moisture and is slightly brittle. She has clogged pores in her scalp and may be allergic to her hair products. She is tender or sensitive on her forehead just above the ends of the eyebrows.
Reading: The tenderness on her head and forehead and the irritation around her eyes are most likely chemically or environmentally related. She is allergic to pets, dogs in particular. She needs to perspire to prevent the clogging of her sweat glands. She also has respiratory problems and easily gets bronchitis, which again is animal-related. A room air purifier will help her more than anything.

F 50 yrs 07-19-98
Problem: She has allergies.
Reading: Emotional and psychological problems are the main cause of her allergies. Eating according to her blood type will help, but the best result will come from working on her emotional state.

F 42 yrs 02-29-99
Problem: She is highly allergic to chemicals and cleaning agents and has a low energy level.
Reading: Her neck has been out of alignment for a long time and needs an adjustment. She would tolerate her allergies better once her neck is adjusted. Her neck is responsible for 30% of her low energy, with chemicals responsible for the remaining 70%.

F 41 yrs 07-20-99
Problem: She has hot flashes when she drinks alcohol.
Reading: This is an allergic reaction to the alcohol. She needs to drink a large glass of water just before drinking the alcohol. This will add

moisture to her liver and digestive organs and minimize the risk of an allergic reaction to the alcohol.

M 7 yrs 12-03-99

Problem: He cries a lot. He was diagnosed with obsessive-compulsive disorder and is taking medication for it. He is allergic to eggs and has had many antibiotics.

Reading: He suffers from sinus problems, which cause headaches, and this is why he cries. His allergies are to airborne pollens, animal hair, dogs, and cats. The sinus pressure causes his ears to clog and ring. His lungs are tight, which is caused by emotion and allergies. He is not well connected spiritually. He should not be on the medication for obsessive-compulsive disorder because it does not help him.

F 35 yrs 12-13-99

Problem: She has had diarrhea for the past 2 years, lasting for 2 weeks at a time. She is on the blood-type diet.

Reading: She is allergic to animal hair and needs a room air purifier. Dog hair is irritating her digestive tract and causing the diarrhea. (She then stated that she has had the dog for 2 years, which is the same span of time that she has had the diarrhea.)

F 50 yrs 03-24-01

Problem: She has environmental allergies, particularly to noxious odors, and has had migraine headaches for the past 30 years.

Reading: There is blocked energy in her forehead extending 1 inch into the hairline. She also has clogged pores in her forehead caused by the blocked energy, which is why she has environmental allergies. This energy block was triggered by fears that she experienced in her early twenties. (She then explained that when she was 21 years of age her husband died and she was left alone with a small child.) She needs psychotherapy to help her overcome her reaction to her husband's death.

F 57 yrs 08-18-01

Problem: When she began menopause 4 years ago, she also developed pin-prick pains at the back of her tongue that have since moved to the left ear, down the left breast, and into the left arm. The pain usually flares up once a month, and she has difficulty swallowing. MRIs, barium swallows, electrocardiograms (ECGs), and thyroid checks have been negative.

Reading: She is having an allergic reaction. Now that her hormones have changed and she no longer has menstrual cycles, her body is more sensitive to airborne pollens. Perhaps she could have a test of her female hormone levels and then try to raise those levels—not because her body requires them but so she will stop reacting to the allergens. Traditional hormone replacement therapy probably would be more effective than acupuncture or herbs.

ALZHEIMER'S DISEASE

F 79 yrs 12-13-99

Problem: She requested a general reading.

Reading: She should stop coloring her own hair because it could affect her brain, causing the Alzheimer's disease. She should either switch to a natural product or stop coloring it altogether.

F 61yrs 10-01-98

Problem: Her father had Alzheimer's disease, and she is concerned that she will get it as well.

Reading: She might get Alzheimer's disease, but eating according to her blood type would minimize brain loss and slow down the disease.

AMYOTROPHIC LATERAL SCLEROSIS (LOU GEHRIG'S DISEASE)

M 37 yrs 08-22-01

Problem: He was diagnosed 1 year ago with amyotrophic lateral sclerosis (ALS). Three years ago his symptoms started with a cold and his speech became affected. Today he has difficulty speaking and has spasms throughout his body. He refuses to take his ALS medication because of the side effects and wonders if a cleaning chemical he uses in his work (he is a mechanic) is the cause of his illness.

Reading: The cause appears to be a virus that got into his bloodstream and settled either in his neck muscles or lymphatic system in his neck and is affecting the drainage there. (His wife then stated that he has had hepatitis C for many years but that the virus has been dormant.) He might try a lymphatic flush or cleansing, neck massage, and even acupuncture to that area. Then he should consult a nutritionist for a very strict diet of vegetables and protein. This will help clean up the blood. The cleaning chemical he uses did not cause the disease, but he might try to avoid it for now. The healthier he keeps his blood the better.

M 63 yrs 08-23-01

Problem: He was diagnosed with ALS 5 months ago. Last year he had twitching in his arms that moved to his stomach and legs. He now lacks control of the muscles of his hands and legs and has trouble with speech and swallowing. He gets around with a walker and is taking an experimental medication. His thyroid gland has tested both hyperactive and hypoactive, and an MRI has shown evidence of some spinal fluid leakage. His career once involved making lead bullets, and tests have shown that he has metal poisoning.

Reading: His ALS was most likely caused by the high exposure to lead. His spleen and liver appear dark and toxic, most likely caused by lead exposure, and the poisoned blood from these organs is causing the twitching throughout his body and affecting his nervous system. His thyroid gland has been damaged by the lead, and the upper lobe is affecting his swallowing and speech. The leaking spinal fluid is also caused by the lead exposure and is an important factor in his strength or weakness. Acupuncture to the areas mentioned may help, but detoxifying the blood in his liver and spleen would bring the best results and may even improve his spinal cord. Once lead is eliminated from his blood, his symptoms could improve greatly.

ANXIETY DISORDERS

M 34 yrs 05-24-99

Problem: He has anxiety attacks when he is extremely tired. He has had trouble sleeping for most of his life (only 3 to 5 hours a night). Tests for sleeping disorders have been negative. He has bad dreams, and he sleepwalks. He wakes up sweating and hyperventilating and cannot determine if he has had a dream or if it was real.

Reading: He has had a nerve dysfunction since childhood that separates the left brain and the right brain more than normal. It may have happened during childbirth or at a young age when he suffered some form of head trauma. This nerve runs from the top center of his head through the center of his face and throat and stops at the base of his neck or upper chest. Medication will not help. He needs reflexology to restore the nerve and other hands-on energy work to open up his forehead. This combination should eliminate the anxiety attacks.

M 35 yrs 07-17-00
Problem: He has had bouts of anxiety for the past 2 years.
Reading: Physically he is in good health, but the anxiety is stress-related. Acupuncture would help initially, and then he should take herbs. Physical exercise would be helpful as well.

ARM/SHOULDER DISCOMFORT

F 65 yrs 12-06-98
Problem: She has had a painful right arm for the past few years. When she was young her arm would go to sleep. The pain is now on the top of the forearm and hand.
Reading: The arm pain is coming from deep in the shoulder, mainly from two areas: under the deltoid muscle and high up under the armpit. She has tendonitis and a lot of scar tissue. This tissue is cutting off the nerve and blood supply to the lower arm. She needs reflexology, acupuncture, and ultrasound. If the problem is not corrected, she could be facing surgery. This problem needs to be treated daily.

F 43 yrs 02-21-99
Problem: She has shoulder discomfort.
Reading: The shoulder has a stretched ligament that runs at a 45-degree angle from the front shoulder across to the outside deltoid. The

shoulder gets stiff when it is cold and feels better when it is warmed up. This is an old injury that has formed scar tissue, which cuts off the blood supply. She needs to rest the shoulder and see a chiropractor for ultrasound treatments.

F 53 yrs 01-10-00

Problem: Her right shoulder bothers her after having lifted something heavy 6 months ago. She has had 1 month of therapy, but it has not helped.

Reading: The right shoulder problem is a soft tissue injury, probably a strained tendon. It runs from the inside of the shoulder and into the chest area. The injury has irritated the outside bursa sack as well. Acupuncture would be the best form of treatment. Ice may help the bursa sack. She should also increase her potassium intake for the soft tissue.

F 34 yrs 05-08-00

Problem: She injured her right shoulder a year ago, and it is still bothering her.

Reading: Her shoulder muscles were tight at the time of the injury, and they were torn. The shoulder should be treated by Rolfing the trapezius muscle and the neck up into the base of skull.

ARTHRITIS

F 34 yrs 05-08-00

Problem: She was diagnosed at 15 years of age with rheumatoid arthritis. She is concerned about the effect her arthritis medication is having on her liver and other organs.

Reading: Eating by her blood type would help her arthritis. If she would detoxify, she could reduce or eliminate her medication. Detoxifying would also prevent the arthritis from getting progressively worse. Her arthritis was caused by chemical exposure when she was between 8 and 14 years of age.

F 50 yrs 07-19-98
Problem: She has arthritis in her right knee and was told that she would need a knee replacement in a few years.
Reading: Although eating better will help her lose weight, it will not help the knee. Shark cartilage oil or apple cider vinegar may help. The knee is not going to get much better, although she can help it from getting much worse.

F 74 yrs 10-25-98
Problem: She has arthritis in the hands and hip.
Reading: Arthritis will get worse in the hands before it gets worse in the hip. The hip problem is chronic; it has been this way for a long time and it does not seem to get much better or worse. Part of the problem in her hand is the lack of strength in the wrist. The ligaments and tendons are tight. Strengthening the wrist will open up blood flow to the hands and increase her hand strength, which will slow down the arthritis. She might try eating according to her blood type to help prevent stiffness of the body and joints.

F 76 yrs 03-13-00
Problem: She has arthritis throughout her body. Her knees and spine bother her the most, and her stomach is often upset.
Reading: She needs to watch her salt intake and eat by her "O" blood-type diet. This will help her stomach and perhaps the arthritis.

F 59 yrs 09-27-99
Problem: She has pain in the lower right side of her neck.
Reading: She has become arthritic in the base of the neck and in the upper back area. Acupuncture will help. Acupuncture to the thyroid

gland also would help stimulate the thyroid, which in turn will improve her neck condition.

F 81 yrs 05-15-00

Problem: She has lower back pain and cold and numb feet.
Reading: Her lumbar vertebrae are arthritic. She could use more minerals and exercise.

F 54 yrs 02-05-01

Problem: She has arthritis in her hands.
Reading: Her gallbladder is sluggish, which is the cause of her hand arthritis.

F 82 yrs 04-16-01

Problem: She has arthritis in the knees and feet, itching on the back, and circulation problems in the left leg. Her chiropractor has worked on these areas for the past 8 years but with little improvement.
Reading: Her blood has become toxic because her liver, pancreas, and gallbladder have not been filtering properly. Acupuncture to these organs would open them up and improve their filtering capabilities. This is the cause of her poor leg circulation, arthritis, and itching. Eating according to her blood type would also improve her blood.

ASTHMA

F 50 yrs 07-19-98

Problem: She is asthmatic and overweight.
Reading: Her emotional and psychological problems are the main reasons she is overweight and asthmatic. She might try eating according

to her blood type, but the best result will come from working on her emotional state. The asthma also will be helped through weight loss.

M 38 yrs 11-30-98

Problem: He has had asthma all his life. Recently he has been using a steroid inhaler with his regular inhaler. In 1986 he was diagnosed with a lung condition called *bronchopulmonary aspergillosis*. He has had pleurisy twice and pneumonia several times throughout his life. He says he never gets sick unless it is lung-related. He gets night chills frequently. He often "cracks" his back and chest area by himself.

Reading: A relationship exists between the asthma and the cracking of the chest and back. The asthma first needs to be approached emotionally, then physically. Psychotherapy and hypnosis would help. Although his asthma was triggered emotionally when he was very young, he did not suffer an isolated trauma but rather a series of emotional events. He was a very sensitive boy, which brought about the trauma. Improvement will come, but it will be gradual yet steady. His dream is to heal himself, but it is only a dream. He has done nothing to help himself. He continues to take the easy way out by taking more medication. He needs reflexology for the respiratory area. The 1986 diagnosis was accurate, but his condition is minor. The steroid inhaler should be substituted with something less toxic.

F 53 yrs 12-06-98

Problem: She has had asthma most of her life. She uses an inhaler for her lungs.

Reading: Her diaphragm needs to be opened up. She needs to do diaphragmatic breathing exercises to improve her asthmatic condition.

F 70 yrs 02-04-01

Problem: She has asthma, bloating, and a lot of stomach acid.

Reading: She is not handling the high fiber and vegetable content of her diet, so she is probably an "O" blood type. (She agreed that she is and stated that she feels better when she follows the blood-type diet and not as well when her diet is high in fiber.) Her asthma is a reaction to the grains that she eats.

M 44 yrs 02-17-01

Problem: He has had asthma since childhood. He uses a steroid inhaler and is concerned that the steroids may be causing problems with his organs. When he exercises or exerts himself, he feels tightness or pain in the kidney area.

Reading: The upper portions of his lungs let the air in but not out. They are tight at the top. Breathing exercises, acupuncture, and reflexology to the lungs would help. The reasons that he feels pain in his back when he exercises are his tightening lungs and tired adrenal glands. He might try using the steroid inhaler less often.

F 59 yrs 03-26-01

Problem: She was diagnosed with asthma 13 years ago and now has a chronic sinus problem. Steroids and antibiotics no longer seem to work. She lost her sense of smell 4 years ago. She had polyps removed in her sinus cavity, and doctors believe that there is another polyp deep in her sinuses that is blocking her ability to smell.

Reading: Her thymus gland is affecting her lymphatic system and her sinus passages. Her asthma is also connected to the thymus gland. Acupuncture to her thymus gland will help these problems and might even restore her sense of smell.

M 43 yrs 04-16-01

Problem: For the past 7 months he has experienced a rapid heart rate of 130 to 140 beats per minute when at rest. Diagnostic tests have all been negative. His doctor told him that he was not at risk and to exercise. A cardiac specialist put him on a beta blocker. He was born with asthma but discontinued the asthma medication because a vitamin C, oat tablet, and copper pill have kept his asthma in check for the past 3 years.

Reading: His lungs may be the cause of his racing heart. They appear to have blood boils or small pockets of blood that rupture and drain back into the heart. When this happens, the rapid heart rate is triggered. Discontinuation of his asthma medication likely has caused the formation of the blood pockets. If he continues use of the asthma inhaler, his heart rate will no longer be irregular. Acupuncture to the lungs also would be helpful for him.

F 41 yrs 07-02-01
Problem: Her lungs are in poor health because she is around fiberglass and cigarette smoke. She has asthma and uses an inhaler off and on. She has bronchitis frequently and takes antibiotics periodically as well. She also takes allergy medications. If she stays on her lung medications, she only becomes ill three to six times per year.
Reading: The bronchioles of the lungs are in worse condition than the lungs themselves. Eating dairy products and poor circulation are contributing to this. Eliminating dairy products is the most important way to improve her health. Acupuncture to her lungs and bronchioles would help as well.

ATTITUDES AND EMOTIONS

M 41 yrs 12-17-99
Problem: He has severe epilepsy for which he has undergone two surgeries. Doctors want to perform another surgical procedure. He has been on several types of medication, but he is depressed and does not take it.
Reading: He is very nervous and full of anxiety. The third surgery will not help unless he first changes his emotional state. Both he and the doctors are too focused on the physical side and not enough on the emotional side. His epilepsy has become progressively worse because his emotional side goes untreated. His occipital area is locked. This area needs to be freed up and the neck muscles relaxed to improve the

epilepsy. The medication is very important for managing and reducing his convulsions.

M 2 yrs 08-23-99

Problem: He is aggressive with his mother and at the daycare center. He bites, chokes, hits, and throws things. He has not yet seen a doctor.
Reading: He has a fear of others. He is like a dog that is a fear biter. He is going to hurt you before you hurt him. He needs to be held by his mother for 2 hours at night, stroked, and spoken to in a calm way. He needs to relax his mind and body at night because he has a hard time relaxing physically when going to bed. Diet does not seem to be a factor during the day, only at night. His mother should avoid giving him sugar and carbohydrates after 5 PM. She could try an herb that creates a calming effect. She can help her son improve. She needs to remain calm but confidant and can see an improvement in 30 days. When he reacts to fear, she needs to react in a very calm way.

F 37 yrs 10-09-97

Problem: She has had kidney infections with vomiting and sweating for 6 months and night chills for 2 weeks. For the past month she has tried everything from herbs to antibiotics but with unsatisfactory results. She struggles with a weight problem. She loves sugar and cannot stop eating it. She has had ovarian pain for years.
Reading: She feels as though she is going to become a victim of something, either an assault or rape. She does not have confidence in men or in relationships and has suffered pain or discomfort during intercourse, which is mentally and physically related. She may have been molested as a child. She has ongoing yeast infections, which are associated with her emotional state. She often feels frightened but for no apparent reason. The kidney infection and her urinary tract infections are related, and they are connected to the yeast infections or reproductive infection. The ovarian pain is very much emotionally related. The vomiting and sweating were normal physical responses to her fear. The sugar cravings are connected to her blood sugar level, which she should monitor. She needs to get plenty of sleep to control her blood sugar

level as well as when experiencing the sugar cravings. She also may suffer from low self-esteem—that she is not good enough at her profession. She needs to seek counseling for the past molestation or sexual experience. This treatment or therapy is important in fixing the current ovarian pain and yeast and kidney infections. She could try a self-defense class, which will help in overcoming her fears and build self confidence.

F 69 yrs 12-21-98

Problem: She is emotional about relationships and animals and cries easily. It is hard for her to cope with turning 70 years of age. She has a fear of not having enough money. This fear started 20 years ago, after her divorce. She also has low self-esteem.

Reading: She is never at peace and her mind never rests because she is afraid she will not have anything to worry about. Therefore she creates problems so she can feel productive and youthful. She needs to embrace her sensitivity with others instead of hiding it. Her emotions and common sense are separated in her brain slightly farther than normal; this physical alignment makes it difficult for her to make decisions. Her entire digestive area has energy blockage. She is a self-healing person. She needs to get out and go dancing. This will open up her emotional side, which will help open up the energy in her digestive system. Her overall physical health is very good.

F 59 yrs 01-11-99

Problem: Part of her colon was removed because of polyps, and since then she has been constipated and has chest pain, chest pressure, and heart palpitations. She had surgery for which she was given a saddle block anesthesia that paralyzed her for 3 days in 1997. One side of her body can become weak, and she must drag one leg to walk.

Reading: She never fully recovered emotionally or physically from the colon surgery. The chest pain is an emotional response to her anticipation of physical pain. She has anxiety attacks from this as well. When she experiences pain she should slow down and work through it. She wants to get even with doctors for the surgery that she has had to suffer through, so she physically develops other ailments. Having surgery has also been a way out of avoiding going back to work, and she has made herself emotionally sick so she does not have to face work.

M 7 yrs 09-27-99

Problem: He has been angry since birth. He has to be told to do things several times and does not do what he is told. He is sensitive and cries a lot.

Reading: He does not have a mental disorder. This behavior is diet-related. He has a lot of congestion in his forehead and chronic headaches because of the pressure. His parents need to watch the processed foods, milk, cheese, sugar, and salt. He is sensitive to processed foods, and the others are giving him forehead congestion. If dietary changes do not work, he should have acupuncture and other energy work. He has a fear of not getting a second chance or of losing something if he lets it go. His fights are mostly the result of fear.

M 15 yrs 09-28-99

Problem: He weighs over twice what he should for his height. He dropped out of school at 10 years of age and has withdrawn from society. He says that he does not want to live. He also has scoliosis and respiratory problems.

Reading: Losing weight would improve his life. He is not really depressed, to any level of concern, but he feels sorry for himself. He is eating and gaining weight for attention. The eating and weight gain are his way of playing a game with himself, his mother, and his doctors. If one were to tell him that his weight gain is a matter of life or death, he would not care because he does not value his life. He is bored and needs to discover something that he cares about so he can believe that his life has value. Once he believes that his life has value, someone could approach him about the weight problem.

He cares a great deal about his mother. Because they are both sick, he has something in common with her and can relate to her illness and have compassion for her. Hearing that he needs to be healthier because his mother and family need his help would help him a lot. This will also help him appreciate himself more.

F 51 yrs 11-12-99

Problem: She has had emotional problems for the past 3 years and cries a lot. She started taking fewer clients and does not know why. She has trouble getting small tasks done, has gained weight, and is tired all the time. She has tried using herbs, but they do not seem to work. She does not sleep well.

Reading: The brain tissue looks irritated, probably from some type of chemical or medication exposure. She has strong energy blockage in both sides of her body. It looks like two long rods that start at the front base of the neck and run down through both lungs and into the outer portion of the digestive area. She should be treated for a chemical exposure rather than for her emotional state. Although her symptoms appear to be caused by emotions, they are physical.

F 53 yrs 12-03-99

Problem: She has high blood pressure, migraine headaches, and mood swings. She is on hormone replacement therapy for menopause and believes that her mood swings are connected to her menstrual periods.

Reading: She is angry and unhappy and has been for some time. The migraine headaches are connected to the anger—she needs to work on this. She is spiritually weak and not well grounded. Prayer will help her relax and become more focused.

F 48 yrs 04-17-00

Problem: She has fibromyalgia, pain, and fatigue. She also has bouts of depression and suicidal tendencies.

Reading: She is angry regarding the past, has an uncontrollable temper, and lacks patience with others. She has an energy flow restriction from the center of her face to the top of her head and down her spine, which is caused by emotions. With acupuncture she will see a 30% immediate improvement in her energy and emotional problems, and then progress will be very slow.

F 58 yrs 05-08-00
Problem: She has chest tightness, hiatal hernia, and bloating.
Reading: She looks alone, afraid, and disappointed. She is struggling emotionally, which is causing most of her physical problems. She should put off the hiatal hernia operation for now because she is not emotionally strong enough for surgery. The stomach bloating is an energy problem. Energy blockage also is in the chest, heart, and upper stomach. Her husband is the primary cause of her emotional state. She would benefit from energy work and acupuncture.

M 15 yrs 01-07-00
Problem: He has an uncontrollable temper and gets into fights at school.
Reading: His problems are strictly emotional. His inner strength is weak, and he has lost touch with his sensitive side. Spiritually he is low. He has a mature side that he can attach to his sensitive side. He would improve by going to a female counselor and having acupuncture, both of which would help open up his inner strength.

F 57 yrs 02-01-99
Problem: She experiences a sensation of motion or earthquake and cannot keep her balance or walk a straight line. When she is lying down she feels as though she is on a waterbed. Doctors cannot find anything wrong, and an MRI was negative. This problem began when she stopped taking her medication for depression.
Reading: The motion in her head is connected to her ears. She has extremely good hearing, and her ear canals are wider than normal. This has caused her to be sensitive to sounds and vibrations. This is not the cause of her motion problem, but it is why she feels the motion. First she needs to muffle the hearing and then work on the cause, which is both emotional and physical. She needs to find the key ingredient in her depression medication and then substitute it with something natural. This should slow down or stop the motion sensation and help her emotional state. She needs spiritual growth and to find a purpose in life. She feels lost and needs to communicate with her family.

F 40 yrs 12-06-98
Problem: She was diagnosed with Graves' disease (hyperthyroid condition) 3 years ago, but a recent thyroid test was negative.
Reading: Her Graves' disease was triggered emotionally when she was in her mid-teens. (She then stated that both of her grandparents died when she was 14 years of age.) She should see a psychotherapist. She has issues from her teen years that she has not dealt with, and she needs to do this so her disease does not get worse or so that it can even improve. One issue in particular will require hypnosis to bring out the emotion and correct it. Once this is accomplished she can begin to heal. She also needs gentle energy work from the top of her head to the bottoms of her feet. Her face is blocked the most. She also should do yogic breathing. She needs more time to herself so she can deal with her emotions. She is at risk for breast or ovarian cancer, but the energy work will play a major role in this outcome.

F 70 yrs 03-01-01
Problem: She has been ill most of her life and has been seen by many doctors. For the past 5 years she has had numbness in her right leg and foot, inability to walk, loss of speech, trembling, and body pain. She has lost the enamel from her teeth and is unable to eat carbohydrates. MRIs and other tests have been negative.
Reading: Bile and toxins have affected her blood because of her liver. Her liver began having problems when she was in her teens and frightened. (She then said that she had a very cruel mother who tied her to her bed and beat her. She wet her bed until the time she was married. Her son died of choking 9 years ago.) Her emotional state caused the liver to shut down. Acupuncture and reflexology to the liver and herbs to flush it would help her. She also needs to see a psychotherapist.

M 49 yrs 01-22-01
Problem: He has been treated with acupuncture for the past 4 years for body tenderness, fatigue, and a stomach disorder. He has seen small improvements, but now surgeons want to repair a valve in his stomach. Stomach acid backs up into his throat and airway.

Reading: He has an energy blockage that runs from the top of his head into his chest. This was caused by an emotional issue that was very serious and occurred when he was a young adult in his early twenties. (He then stated that when he was in his early twenties a car struck and killed his mother.) He has not sufficiently dealt with this death emotionally, and it has manifested itself in his body. He needs acupuncture and energy work, starting first with the energy work. Treatment should start at the top of the head and gradually work down so that he can handle the treatments. Hypnotherapy should unlock some of the illness if the energy treatments are successful. He might delay surgery for about a month to see if hypnotherapy and energy work improve his digestive disorder.

F 54 yrs 03-18-01

Problem: She has wheat intolerance and migraine headaches.

Reading: The two problems are connected. Her breathing is very shallow, and there are not sufficient levels of blood and oxygen being pumped into the digestive system after eating to enable proper digestion of wheat (or any other food for that matter). This lack of oxygen in the blood is contributing to the migraine headaches as well. She is suppressing her emotions and hurt, which is suppressing her diaphragm. She needs to learn diaphragmatic breathing or take up yoga. She also should work on the issue from her early childhood that caused the shallow breathing.

F 51 yrs 04-23-01

Problem: She has chronic anger. She had a hysterectomy 20 years ago and has been angry ever since. She wants to know why she is so angry and what she can do to about it. For the past 4 years doctors have prescribed an antidepressant to help control her anger. Before the antidepressant she was nice one minute and would become angry the next as though she were two different people.

Reading: Something happened during her early school years. Perhaps a teacher approached her sexually. (She said that when she was 7 years of age a 15-year-old cousin molested her.) This is the source of her distrust and anger. She needs psychotherapy for this molestation. She also needs spiritual growth, but she should make sure it is the right kind for her. She needs the outdoors, fresh air, sunlight, and laughter.

M 60 yrs 06-09-01

Problem: He is concerned about depression. He has tried an antidepressant and other medications but is off them now. He has anger occasionally, but meditation helps it go away.

Reading: His pituitary gland may contribute to 25% to 30% of his depression because of occasional low levels of hormones governed by this gland. However, the rest of his depression and anger is a learned behavior that began around 9 to 10 years of age. His current level of meditation is helping him deal with his current anger but not with the deeper issues of anger from his childhood. For those issues he needs to take his meditation deeper. Psychotherapy would be good for that as well. Also, his liver is toxic and should be detoxified. This is where he carries his anger.

F 20 yrs 07-02-01

Problem: She has been battling depression since she was 10 years of age and currently is taking an antidepressant. She dropped out of school at 13 years of age. She has attempted suicide, began having panic attacks at 16 years of age, and did not leave the house for a year. She is now trying to socialize again and finish school, but she gets dizzy, sleeps a lot, and has short-term memory loss.

Reading: She wanted everything to be perfect, including her parents' marriage. Her depression at 10 years of age was really an attitude or behavior to try to keep them together. She is neither clinically nor chemically depressed. She has an energy blockage to the throat, thyroid, thymus, lungs, and reproductive area. Acupuncture to these blocked areas and discontinuation of the antidepressant would improve her energy and fatigue. In addition, she should have psychological and behavioral treatments as follows: (1) positive reinforcement tapes and psychotherapy to reinforce positive behavior, (2) acupuncture treatments to the energy-blocked areas, (3) daily reflexology; and (4) physical exercises such as yoga, martial arts, or tai chi.

AUTISM

M 9 yrs 01-06-01

Problem: He displays autistic behavior. He flicks his hands and is disinterested in things around him. He also has a digestive disorder, toxic blood, and leaky gut syndrome. His hearing is normal, but he cannot determine the locations of sounds.

Reading: His lower stomach is not functioning properly because the blood in his stomach moves upward. He has headaches in his forehead, and he prefers to sleep on his back because of headaches, energy blockage, and congestion in his forehead and face. He has a blood issue, not a nerve disorder. His pituitary gland has been affected by his diet and toxic blood. Rolfing, acupuncture, and reflexology would help his energy move properly. A vaccination that he was given at a young age caused this disorder.

M 6 yrs 11-27-00

Problem: He was diagnosed with Asperger's syndrome, a form of autism, and is slightly uncoordinated.

Reading: His pancreas and gallbladder cause 60% of his problems. These organs are not functioning normally and have struggled since birth, most likely because of a drug given at that time. He would benefit from herbs and acupuncture to the pancreas and gallbladder to help treat and restore these organs.

M 12 yrs 08-01-01

Problem: He was diagnosed with mild to moderate mental retardation. His mother believes that he is more in the autism category. He cannot read or write and cannot or will not speak. When he was 4 years of age an MRI was normal. He also gets chronic ear infections.

Reading: His brain and body development appears to be normal, but he has very little energy running through his body and because of this he is not well grounded. This was present at birth. (His mother then stated that he was 2 months premature.) He needs energy work, acupuncture, and even reflexology to stimulate his energy, starting at the top of his head and progressing to the bottoms of his feet. First he needs to open up and create energy flow from head to toe, and then that energy needs to be connected. This will help him become more whole emotionally and physically and instill in him the desire to try harder. This energy blockage also causes his ear infections and sinus infections under one eye. He appears capable of doing more than he does. His parents should try exercising his brain with simple card games and picture cards with words.

M 4 yrs 10-07-01

Problem: He was diagnosed with autism 1 year ago. He does not speak and has difficulty understanding and concentrating. Doctors suggested speech therapy, but it did not work. His mother wants to know what she can do to bring him out of this emotional state because he is fine physically.

Reading: She needs to show him love, give him a lot of hugs, and perhaps get a mid-sized dog for him as a companion. She should avoid trying to teach him things–she should just show him. She might show him comedy-type movies that would hold his attention and encourage him to laugh. Possibly he is low in a hormone that helps brain development, so she should consult a specialist about this. His energy looks normal on one side of his brain and sunken on the other side. This suppressed energy needs to be moved in an upward motion, starting at the chin. Creating some space on this side of the brain would enable his brain to develop once the hormone is replaced.

BACK (SPINE, VERTEBRAL) DISORDERS

F 39 yrs 06-20-00
Problem: She has chronic back pain.
Reading: Her kidneys are weak and a factor in her back pain. She needs more water, cranberry juice, and a lot of other liquids. If she increases her fluids by 70%, she will have less back pain.

F 43 yrs 11-02-98
Problem: The arch in her foot is painful; an arch support has not helped.
Reading: One of her lumbar disks is twisted, and the pain is radiating down the leg and affecting the arch. Her ankle and shin on the left leg are irritated, and the tailbone is twisted because of the lumbar problem. A chiropractic adjustment would help this problem.

F 51 yrs 10-19-98
Problem: She has had neck, back, and shoulder pain for 9 years. She also has headaches and pain in her hip and down both legs.
Reading: The shoulder and back pain are soft-tissue–related, not structural. She has severe muscle spasms. The main area of spasm is in the thorax between the shoulders. She also has a vertebra that will not stay in alignment until the spasms are corrected. Her cervical vertebrae need adjustment also. They have caused the entire neck to be in spasm and are the main reason for the headaches and lack of sleep. The lower back is twisted and in spasm at the lower lumbar and pelvic areas. A chiropractor needs to fix the thoracic area first, and the neck and lower back will respond better. Diet is not a factor; minerals and vitamins are at normal levels.

F 62 yrs 12-20-98
Problem: Her hip and leg muscles ache and have become weak. Doctors cannot diagnose the problem. The skin on her buttocks itches so much that it burns at times.
Reading: The pain in the hips and legs is coming from the mid-lumbar area. Rolfing can help this. The source is a disk that has been slightly compressed and slipped forward. This has caused nerve interference and is also the reason for her itchy skin.

F 48 yrs 03-14-99
Problem: She has shooting pains throughout her body. An MRI has revealed four bulging disks in her neck. Doctors say her spinal canal is too narrow (spinal stenosis) and pinching a nerve.
Reading: She has been exposed to chemicals that have affected her brain. (She then stated that she worked in a plastics factory.) The most affected area is from the side of the head up near where she parts her hair down into the back of the skull. The spinal fluid pressure is causing nerve disruption. The four disks in her neck may have ruptured because of the spinal fluid pressure, or there may be no real rupture; just the spinal fluid pressure might be causing the disks to bulge. She needs to see a neurologist and a naturopath. She should drink plenty of water and liquid vegetables to help detoxify her body. She should use a sauna three to four times a week for 2 weeks and avoid chemicals irritants (e.g., perfume) or hair products before the sauna. She also should avoid dying her hair for 60 days. Body products with a natural base would be fine for her, however.

M 44yrs 06-29-99
Problem: He has had lower back pain for the past 6 weeks.
Reading: The problem in his lower back is muscular, not structural. One side of the back has more spasms than the other side, and the back is being twisted or pulled in two directions. He has lost his confidence that his health will improve, but he will regain it if he continues the physical therapy. He needs to exercise and strengthen the lower back. Rolfing, ice, and heat would help as well.

F 46 yrs 10-18-99
Problem: She has severe back pain. Today she had trouble standing and was crying.
Reading: Her back pain is soft-tissue–related, mostly muscle spasms. She likely has rectal pain as well because most of her lower back pain is coming from a condition in the rectum. She should see a doctor who could treat both the rectal area and the lower back.

F 81 yrs 05-15-00
Problem: She has lower back pain and feet that are numb and cold.
Reading: Her last cervical vertebra and the first and fifth lumbar vertebrae are arthritic. She could use more minerals and exercise.

F 58 yrs 02-21-00
Problem: Her leg goes numb; she believes that she has a pinched nerve in her back.
Reading: She can relieve the nerve in her back by exercising and breathing properly every day.

F 21 yrs 09-13-99
Problem: She has scoliosis.
Reading: The scoliosis is minor and not a setback, but it will get worse without exercise. She needs to exercise her legs, which will strengthen her back without putting pressure on it. Her lower lumbar disks are degenerating. Eating by her blood type would help her a lot.

F 43 yrs 09-20-00
Problem: She has chronic back pain. She injured her back 20 years ago and ruptured a lumbar disk.
Reading: She has very tight muscles in her lower back. She has back spasms, and the muscles twist in both directions. Potassium and other minerals could help her. She also needs acupuncture, reflexology, and deep massage. The soft tissue should be worked first, and then the vertebrae.

F 26 yrs 02-19-01

Problem: She has endometriosis with large clots on the uterus and right ovary. She is taking injections to prevent her menstrual periods. She wants to know what is causing the endometriosis and the best treatment. She also has knee displacement.

Reading: Her knee displacement is related to her hips, which are displaced as well, throwing her lumbar area and upper torso forward. The lumbar area is weak, which is stirring the blocked energy in the center of her brain, causing confusion, impaired decision-making, and nervousness. The stressed nerves in her lower back cause the endometriosis. She needs adjustment and treatments to her lower back, followed by acupuncture and reflexology for her brain. Then she needs Rolfing for her pelvic area, followed by chiropractic treatments to that area.

M 57 yrs 06-30-01

Problem: He has had chronic lower back pain for 40 years. He has had three lumbar disk surgeries and wears a morphine patch to help control the pain. He wants to know why his back pain is still so severe.

Reading: He has suffered trauma to his face up under the chin or nose that forced his head back and into the brainstem, causing nerve damage to the spinal cord. This is causing his back pain. His problem is nerve disruption—not a disk problem. (He said that he had concussions from high school football, motorcycle accidents, and fistfights.) Most likely the football injury is the cause of his back pain because he has had pressure on his brainstem for a long time. He should have cranial work—Rolfing or acupuncture—to the base of his skull to move the head forward and thus relieve pressure on the nerves in the brainstem and spinal cord.

F 58 yrs 06-11-01

Problem: She has had osteoarthritis in her hips and spine for 7 years. Walking is painful, and her muscles ache from the waist down.

Reading: The back of her skull has been affected by cigarette smoke, causing pain down the neck and upper back and in her lower back as well. Nicotine is irritating her blood. This in turn is bothering her upper lungs, the back of her head, and her spinal cord. She should have acupuncture to the back of her head and neck and the upper back, and she should quit smoking. Her thyroid was affected by smoking as well. (She said that doctors removed her thyroid gland 8 years ago, but she insists that she is only a light smoker.)

F 79 yrs 08-20-01
Problem: She has had lower back problems for the past 20 years. She was diagnosed with spinal stenosis, has had a laminectomy, and now uses a walker because of a lack of balance, weakness in her left leg, and numbness in her toes. For a while she dragged her left foot, but acupuncture treatments have helped that problem. When she walks she is bent over because of lumbar pain, but when she sits the pain goes away.

Reading: Her spinal condition is caused mainly by a lack of calcium and her pancreas not releasing enough insulin. She also lacks energy flow through the spine. Acupuncture to the cervical spine would help open up that energy. Treating the pancreas with acupuncture and perhaps prescribing insulin would increase insulin into the bloodstream enough to restore the spine and enable her to regain enough strength so that she can walk better.

F 48 yrs 09-05-01
Problem: She has had three back surgeries for ruptured disks, but she still has upper and lower back pain as well as pain in her hip. She no longer wants to work and has gained 50 pounds from just lying around.

Reading: Lack of exercise and weight gain are major factors in her back pain. Her hormones are slightly low because of inactivity and age, which is causing her bones to become thin and soft. She might need only exercise, but she could increase her hormones as well. She lacks the will or desire to improve her health and is depressed about her personal life. She needs positive reinforcement and friends who enjoy exercise, walking, hiking, and sports. She is also slightly low in essential vitamins. Taking these vitamins, stretching, and drinking plenty of water will also help her back.

F 61 yrs 10-13-01
Problem: She has back pain just below the shoulder blades that can move around to her front. She has had this pain off and on for 6 years, and it returned 3 months ago. Her pain is so intense that her doctors have her on a morphine drip.
Reading: Her lungs are causing this problem. Specifically, when blood leaves the lungs it passes through narrowed capillaries. (When asked whether she smokes, she said that she does.) Smoking has damaged and narrowed her capillaries, and she is experiencing circulatory pain when blood and oxygen exit the lungs.

BALANCE PROBLEMS

M 44 yrs 06-29-99
Problem: He has had a chronic whistle in the right ear for the last 3 years. Six months ago he lost his balance and could not get out of bed.
Reading: His sinus passages are very narrow, even up through the forehead. He could use energy work to the back of his head and neck. His ears ring less when they are dry than when they are wet. The ringing is structural, not nerve-related. This may be fixed with surgery.

M 54 yrs 01-27-01
Problem: He has had light-headedness with loss of balance for 6 months. His neurologist believes that he may have diabetes. He now suffers from headaches and numbness in the right side of his head, and he is very tired.
Reading: He has a "V"-shaped, deep energy blockage on the top of his head that appears to have a nerve-brain connection. This is a disruption

caused by electrical airwaves, perhaps because of mobile phones, antennas, or high-power voltage. If exposure is eliminated he has an 80% chance of total recovery. If he does not eliminate the exposure he will continue to get worse. He needs energy opened up from the navel up and out through the digestive system, lungs, chest, and shoulders. This will prevent any future disorder. He needs acupuncture to the brain for the nerve disorder and acupuncture to the body for energy. (He then explained that he works at the airport, where many electronic waves are present.)

F 57 yrs 02-01-99

Problem: She experiences a sensation of motion or earthquake and cannot keep her balance or walk a straight line. When she is lying down she feels as though she is on a waterbed. Doctors cannot find anything wrong, and an MRI was negative. This problem began when she stopped taking her medication for depression.

Reading: The motion in her head is connected to her ears. She has extremely good hearing, and her ear canals are wider than normal. This has caused her to be sensitive to sounds and vibrations. This is not the cause of her motion problem, but it is why she feels the motion. First she needs to muffle the hearing and then work on the cause, which is both emotional and physical. She needs to find the key ingredient in her depression medication and then substitute it with something natural. This should slow down or stop the motion sensation and help her emotional state.

BLADDER/URINARY TRACT PROBLEMS

F 74 yrs 10-25-99
Problem: She cannot control her urine flow.
Reading: The muscles around the pelvic area are weak. She needs to learn how to exercise her pelvic muscles (Kegel exercises).

F 61 yrs 10-01-98
Problem: She believes that she has a urinary or bladder infection because she has a burning sensation after urination.
Reading: She does not have a urinary infection, but her bladder is very depleted of liquid. She should stop consuming caffeine for a while and drink more liquids.

F 50 yrs 05-20-99
Problem: She has had blood in her urine for the past 3 months. She has been taking antibiotics for this condition, but the blood is still present.
Reading: The blood in her urine is coming from the liver (60% possibility) or the lower portion of her kidneys (40% possibility). This was started by an infection that went untreated and now has settled in her liver.

M 43 yrs 05-18-97
Problem: He has very low urinary output.
Reading: He simply does not drink enough water. He must increase his water intake to three times the amount he currently consumes.

F 51 yrs 07-19-97
Problem: She is urinating in small amounts.
Reading: She needs to drink more water. Water will increase her urinary flow and help prevent urinary tract infections.

F 43 yrs 09-20-00
Problem: She tore a pelvic ligament 3 years ago while skiing. She may be facing bladder surgery because of this condition.
Reading: Rolfing should be used on the pelvic area. She has a strained or torn ligament causing pain to the groin. Correcting this ligament problem may help the bladder.

M 44 yrs 01-08-01
Problem: He has had urinary and bladder problems for 16 years.
Reading: The bladder looks heavy and swollen. Cutting out salt would likely help his bladder.

F 73 yrs 03-10-01
Problem: Her feet became paralyzed 1 year ago, but MRI and x-ray examinations are negative. She is now incontinent of urine and lacks bladder control.
Reading: Her bladder control and foot condition are caused by her adrenal glands. She needs to see an endocrinologist. Her hormone level has affected her neurologic system. She has too much salt in her system, and this combined with the hormone and adrenal problem, is affecting her bladder.

F 74 yrs 02-16-01
Problem: She urinates frequently. Bladder tests have all been negative.
Reading: Her bladder problem is a result of a back problem. A vertebra is pressing on a nerve that controls the bladder. She should see a chiropractor or acupuncturist for treatment.

F 29 yrs 04-21-01
Problem: Her bladder, small intestine, uterus, and rectum were pro-

lapsed. To repair them, surgeons removed her left ovary and uterus. She now has had throbbing bladder pain for 3 years. About 2 years ago doctors diagnosed it as interstitial cystitis, a disease of the bladder lining. When urine enters the bladder, she has excruciating pain. She also has to urinate 60 times a day. She is taking a medication that rebuilds the bladder lining. Acupuncture has not helped, and massage therapy helps the stress but not the bladder pain.

Reading: An insect may have stung her and its poison entered her spinal fluid, after which it entered the intestinal tract and then the bladder. (She agreed that she was bitten on the leg and it swelled up severely.) Acupuncture to the bladder likely would help her.

F 59 yrs 05-19-01

Problem: She had a prolapsed bladder and bowel 8 years ago. The bowel was repaired, but doctors want to delay surgery on the bladder until it gets worse. The soft spot on the top of her head has been tender since her teen years, and her eyesight is poor as well.

Reading: The problem with her soft spot, eyesight, bladder, and bowel is a mineral and vitamin deficiency, most likely acquired from one of her parents before she was born. (She then explained that she was a twin and was delivered a month early because of her mother's uremic poisoning.) She needs tests to determine mineral and vitamin levels so that they can be corrected accordingly. It would also help her to lie on a recline board (her head lower than her feet) at a 45-degree angle and perform Kegel (hold and release) exercises while in this position.

BLOATING, GAS

F 58 yrs 05-08-00
Problem: She has stomach bloating.
Reading: Her bloating is an energy problem. She has energy blockage in the chest, heart, and upper stomach. Her condition would improve with acupuncture or hands-on energy work to these areas.

F 47 yrs 01-28-98
Problem: She has stomach bloating that comes and goes.
Reading: She needs to cut back on her vegetable intake. She also needs more fat in her diet, particularly when experiencing the bloating. Her digestive system is fast-paced. She should eat foods that will process and digest more slowly because her body is not getting all the nutrients it needs from the food.

F 60 yrs 03-03-98
Problem: She is concerned about her digestion and elimination.
Reading: Her colon is often full of gas, possibly caused by the gallbladder. She should have her gallbladder examined and probably flushed, which would have a positive result. Reflexology would also help the gallbladder.

F 61 yrs 10-01-98
Problem: She has frequent stomach bloating.
Reading: The bloating is yeast-related. She should have her yeast condition treated, perhaps by a naturopath for a more natural approach to treatment.

F 53 yrs 03-23-00
Problem: She has had a strange feeling in her intestine for 2 months. She was treated for ulcers and had several tests, but the tests are negative and ulcer treatment has not helped.
Reading: Gases are trapped in her colon. She needs to be on a liquid diet for 1 to 3 days, perhaps under the care of a naturopath. This will clear up the colon and decrease the gases. She also needs to eat by her blood type and avoid caffeine.

F 59 yrs 12-21-98
Problem: She gets severely bloated, and she has had constipation and diarrhea all her life. Doctors have not been able to determine what is wrong with her colon. At one time she could not have a bowel movement for 3 months.
Reading: Most of her problem is in the stomach and surrounding organs and colon. The small intestine does not seem to be as affected. This is mostly a nerve interference problem. She needs to see a chiropractor for adjustment of a vertebra in her back just above the kidneys. She also needs Rolfing and reflexology. These practitioners need to concentrate on the stomach, gallbladder, spleen, liver, and other organs before they begin work on the colon. They should avoid the colon until some of the tenderness leaves this area. She should see a psychotherapist after 30 days of Rolfing and reflexology. Her emotional state has caused a lot of energy blockage in the stomach and midsection. She wants to avoid the emotional end, but it cannot be avoided. She needs to drink plenty of water. The Rolfing and reflexology will give her a 30% improvement. She will then require psychotherapy and continued energy work before she can progress further.

F 50 yrs 05-20-99
Problem: She has had stomach pains and bloating for the past 2 weeks. She thinks that her stomach pain is a result of having taken antibiotics and is now treating it with an herb.
Reading: The pain stems from her colon, and it moves from side to side. The bloating is caused by irritation and inflammation, not by a

reaction to the antibiotic. She may have a fairly large blockage in the colon that is serious. This could be an ulcer, polyp, or tumor, but most likely it is a malignant tumor. This blockage is causing severe inflammation and hence the bloating. She needs to see a gastric surgeon.

F 58 yrs 07-20-99

Problem: She has left side pain under the ribcage that comes across or under the breast. She belches a lot, and it relieves the pain. She has had this pain for over 15 years. A naturopath is treating her with acupuncture, but she is not getting better.

Reading: She does not have stomach or colon problems. The problem stems from the adrenal gland over her left kidney. The kidney looks good, but it does have pressure on it. She has a tumor either on the adrenal gland or between the adrenal gland and the kidney. She needs blood work and other diagnostic tests taken of this area.

F 44yrs 11-18-99

Problem: She has excessive gas in the colon.

Reading: Her colon looks fine. She needs to eliminate carbonated beverages from her diet.

F 54 yrs 03-15-99

Problem: She has a history of digestive disorders, including gas and bloating in the colon. She has been diagnosed with celiac disease (gluten intolerance).

Reading: She has a blockage to the upper center of the colon. She needs energy work on the colon, upper stomach, liver, and gallbladder straight up through the center of her chest. She also needs to take an herbal enzyme. Her digestive enzymes are depleted because of radiation exposure. She also needs to detoxify herself from the radiation. A naturopath would be able to treat the enzyme problem and help her detoxify.

F 55 yrs 05-15-00

Problem: She has severe bloating.

Reading: She needs a lower gastrointestinal series. She has a blockage that may be more serious than just a transient bowel disorder.

F 70 yrs 02-04-01

Problem: She has bloating and a lot of stomach acid.

Reading: She reacts to the high fiber and vegetable content of her diet and is probably an "O" blood type. (She confirmed that she is an "O" blood type and said that she feels better when she is on the blood-type diet and less well when she eats foods that are high in fiber.)

F 45 yrs 10-30-00

Problem: She has a lot of gas after eating a meal.

Reading: Certain vegetables and fruits are causing the gas that she gets after meals.

M 54 yrs 05-12-01

Problem: For the past 10 years he has been unable to pass gas except during a bowel movement. He can feel his colon backing up with gas, but he cannot release it.

Reading: He does not use his diaphragm when he breathes, and therefore his small intestine is trapping the gases in his colon. He needs to breathe using his diaphragm.

BLOOD DISORDERS

M 62 yrs 06-08-99

Problem: He requested a general reading.

Reading: His red blood cells look depleted. They lack minerals and oxygen and possibly vitamins. Apple cider vinegar would help.

F 33 yrs 11-07-98
Problem: She is pregnant with twins, and her blood platelet level results came back low. She wonders why her platelet levels are low and if she is at risk for major bleeding during delivery.
Reading: She is very tired and has darkness under her eyes. Stress is causing part of the fatigue. Some of this stress is caused by personal or relationship issues. The blood lacks oxygen, minerals, and vitamins. The low platelet count will not likely affect the pregnancy, but her blood is being affected by the stress. Although she is not a bleeder, she will lose a considerable amount of blood during delivery. Her blood count will return to normal after the pregnancy. The twins look very healthy.

F 49 yrs 12-13-99
Problem: She is anemic (low RBC count) and very tired.
Reading: She is a strong candidate for eating by her blood type. This diet would help her anemia.

F 62 yrs 06-30-01
Problem: She was diagnosed with a rare blood disorder in which the white blood cells (WBCs) build up, causing major fatigue, and then are eliminated after about 2 weeks, when she feels well again. Doctors do not know what causes it or how to treat it. She also suffers from chronic headaches across the forehead and temples, for which she takes aspirin. She can feel the tension pulling her head backward, and this makes her neck sore.
Reading: Either the WBCs are causing a kidney or bladder dysfunction, or the kidneys are causing the blood disorder; the latter is more likely. When the blood to the kidneys does not flow normally, this affects the blood in her spine, which drains or reduces the blood flow to the head and causes the light headaches. The tension that she is feeling in her forehead and neck is actually the lack of blood flow. She is feeling a draining of blood going back down her head and traveling down the spine. Her condition is analogous to holding a water hose upright and not having enough water pressure to force the water out

through the top so that it travels back down the hose. Acupuncture might fix the kidney and bladder problem, and this in turn could fix the WBC problem.

F 50 yrs 08-09-01

Problem: She has a low WBC count. Doctors do not know why this has occurred, but they suspect that a virus was the cause. She lacks energy and resistance to infection.

Reading: Radiation treatment disrupted her adrenal glands and altered her WBC count. Because her adrenal glands are exhausted, her energy is very low. Even her lungs are involved. She needs reflexology for her lungs and adrenal glands and acupuncture and herbs for her adrenal glands.

F 63 yrs 10-11-01

Problem: She was diagnosed with fibromyalgia and has had 8 years of chronic body pain. Her legs are her main problem—she can walk only a few steps at a time. She has a rare RBC disorder that doctors believe is causing her leg problems. She is also very fatigued and unable to work because of her condition.

Reading: The lining of her lungs looks irregular, as though she were exposed to a chemical burn or smoke inhalation. This caused her lungs not to filter blood properly and resulted in her blood being poisoned. Blood passing through the digestive tract is not much better; by the time it reaches her legs, it is in its worst condition, with the RBCs nearly depleted. Her lung condition caused both the RBC disorder and the fibromyalgia. She needs to increase the oxygen levels in her blood. (She then stated that she has been smoking since she was a little girl.)

BLOOD PRESSURE PROBLEMS

F 53 yrs 12-03-99
Problem: She has high blood pressure and is on hormone replacement therapy.
Reading: The high blood pressure is caused by the hormone medication.

F 52 yrs 12-13-99
Problem: Her blood pressure is out of control at times.
Reading: She needs to see a therapist to learn how to bring the mind and body together. She will need medication for the blood pressure and a natural product, such as St. John's Wort, for calming. After taking this herb she can begin learning how to relax. Her hormone levels are good, but she needs to switch the brand of hormone she is using. This may be causing her blood pressure problem. If switching does not regulate her blood pressure, the dosage should be lowered.

F 73 yrs 09-05-99
Problem: She has high blood pressure for which she is taking medication.
Reading: She needs to see a cardiologist for her heart, which is weaker on the right side than on the left. She also should pay more attention to her diet. Decreasing fats and salt would enable her to lower the dose of her blood pressure medication, which is too high for her.

M 55 yrs 02-11-01

Problem: He has had high blood pressure for 20 years. He meditates and has been on medications and chelation therapy, but nothing has been able to control it. Currently he is having sinus problems.

Reading: His heart and aorta look fine, but his liver looks toxic and is slightly enlarged. He needs energy work to the liver, including acupuncture and reflexology. He should also have a liver flush and watch his fat intake. Apple cider vinegar would be good for his liver. His sinus condition is connected to his liver problem.

M 61 yrs 03-26-01

Problem: He has had high blood pressure for 25 years and wants to know what is causing it.

Reading: The liver is causing his high blood pressure, probably as a result of excessive alcohol intake over 25 years ago. Acupuncture and an herbal flush to the liver would help his condition. Eating according to his blood type would be very beneficial as well.

F 38 yrs 07-11-01

Problem: She has joint and muscle pain in her shoulders, neck, arms, elbows, and knees. She also has had high blood pressure for the past 3 months for which she is taking medication.

Reading: She lacks a mineral for joint cartilage—likely it is sulfur, but she needs a consultation about this. Her kidneys need sulfur to function better; this would prevent the joint and muscle aches and keep her blood pressure under control.

BLOOD SUGAR PROBLEMS

F 37 yrs 10-09-97
Problem: She is overweight; she loves sugar and cannot seem to stop eating it.
Reading: She needs to learn to control her emotions. She should monitor her blood sugar level because it is a factor in the sugar cravings. Getting plenty of sleep when she suffers from sugar cravings will help her control both.

F 43 yrs 11-02-98
Problem: She has chronic bone and joint pain and stomach and gall-bladder problems.
Reading: The bone and joint pain is related to her high blood sugar level, which is causing the digestive problems. She is very close to becoming diabetic.

BREAST PROBLEMS

F 43 yrs 04-23-96
Problem: She asked for a general reading.
Reading: She has tenderness near the breastbone that runs across the chest to one breast. She has two dark spots inside one breast, which she

needs to have examined. She should avoid using underarm deodorants and allow her body to breathe and perspire naturally.

F 51 yrs 02-17-98

Problem: She has lumps in her breast.

Reading: She has a few hard fatty lumps in her breasts, one breast having more than the other. These lumps are of no threat. Her breasts look healthy. She should see a naturopath to help change her diet so she can prevent more fatty lumps from forming in the breasts.

F 38 yrs 12-02-99

Problem: She was recently diagnosed with a breast lump that was benign; she also has gum problems.

Reading: The pituitary gland looks exhausted. This is a factor in the gum and breast problems. She needs to learn how to relax and meditate, which will help the pituitary gland.

F 47 yrs 05-15-00

Problem: She gets a pain under her left breast when she is under stress. Her blood pressure is borderline high.

Reading: The pain under her left breast is related to her hormones, not to blood pressure or stress. Her hormone levels need to be balanced.

F 21 yrs 10-27-96

Problem: She has lumps in her breast.

Reading: Her menstrual cycle is off, and her ovaries are not in balance with each other. She would have fewer breast lumps if her cycle were more regulated.

F 56 yrs 11-18-99

Problem: She has a clogged lymph node under her arm. She is concerned about breast cancer. She is on synthetic hormone replacement therapy.

Reading: The outer portion of her breast has some dark fiber or tough-looking tissue, although no evidence of cancer exists. She should use a natural hormone instead.

F 45 yrs 01-31-99
Problem: She has sensitive breasts.
Reading: She should eat according to her blood type. She is caffeine intolerant, and her breasts become very sensitive when she ingests it. She needs to have regular breast examinations as well.

F 35 yrs 07-06-99
Problem: Her breasts are lactating, but she is not pregnant.
Reading: The base of her throat is swollen, which was caused by a soft tissue trauma. (She then stated that 2 months earlier she had a whiplash injury.) The pituitary gland suffered trauma and is not functioning normally, which is why her breasts are lactating. This can be corrected by treating the pituitary gland with acupuncture and other energy work.

F 45 yrs 10-30-00
Problem: Her left breast is painful, sore, hard to the touch, and red, and it flares up around the time of her menstrual periods. The breast improved after treatment with acupuncture, but the pain returned with her last period. She had breast cancer 3 years ago, and part of the breast was removed.
Reading: She should have an examination, mammogram, or ultrasound. She has a small, malignant tumor just below and outside the nipple. This tumor is in the breast tissue, not in the blood or bone. She also had an energy blockage from the pubic line upward through the digestive tract and up through the breast in a "V" shape. She needs energy work in that area.

F 40 yrs 11-21-00
Problem: She has pain and tenderness in her breasts.
Reading: Her breasts are tender because her pituitary gland is exhausted and has affected the release of her hormones. Reflexology and herbs

would help her. She could suffer from damage to the breast ducts in 5 years if this problem persists.

F 55 yrs 03-26-01
Problem: She had a lump in her right breast a year ago that was negative for cancer on a mammogram. The lump is near her armpit, and it aches and burns at times. Her family has a history of cancer, and she is concerned about it. She wears an estrogen patch.
Reading: The lump is not cancerous, but it is hot and irritated. This comes and goes with her hormones, which kick on and off during the day. She needs to balance her hormones, and this problem should calm down. The patch she is wearing is not strong enough to be effective later in the day when she becomes tired and stressed.

CANDIDA/YEAST INFECTION

F 42 yrs 07-26-98
Problem: She has frequent yeast infections.
Reading: Her yeast infections are related to stress and tight clothing. Drinking more water and opening her sweat glands by inducing sweating (e.g., with saunas) will improve or help control the yeast infections.

F 37 yrs 10-09-97
Problem: She believes that emotions play a large part in her physical problems, which include kidney and yeast infections.
Reading: She feels as though she is going to become a victim of something, either an assault or rape. She does not have confidence in men or in relationships and may have been molested as a child. She has ongoing yeast infections, which are associated with her emotional state. She

often feels frightened for no apparent reason. She needs to seek counseling for the past molestation or sexual experience. This treatment or therapy is very important in relieving the yeast and kidney infections. She could try a self-defense class, which will help in overcoming her fear of becoming a victim.

F 61 yrs 10-01-98

Problem: She has frequent stomach bloating.

Reading: The bloating is yeast-related. She should be treated for the yeast condition, perhaps with natural supplements. She might consult a naturopath for treatment.

M 47 yrs 02-09-01

Problem: He has an ongoing rash in the groin area; he was diagnosed with candidiasis 15 years ago.

Reading: The glands in his body look clogged, particularly in the groin. His blood looks dark and it is likely caused by the candidiasis. He needs to open his sweat glands, which will help the candidiasis. Hot mineral or salt baths, hot saunas, or steam baths and drinking warm water or carbonated water would be good. Cold beverages would shut down his energy and should be avoided. His spleen has been affected by the candidiasis but should clear up with the bathing.

F 57 yrs 09-04-00

Problem: She has had periodic yeast and bacterial infections to the vaginal area for the past 20 years. She experienced a salt-type burning to this area 2 weeks ago. She has had this problem before, but this was the most intense. Hormone supplements have not helped. Everything aggravates this area, including toilet tissue and creams.

Reading: She has an infection or blockage in the fallopian tube. (She then stated that she had a tubal ligation 20 years ago.) Having her tubes tied has brought on the vaginal discomfort because of a lack of body fluids and important nutrients reaching this area. This is causing the salt-type burning effect. Most likely she has scar tissue from having had this procedure. (She commented that the tubal ligation was done with a larger incision.)

CHEMICALS/POISONS, REACTIONS TO

F 34 yrs 05-08-00
Problem: She was diagnosed with rheumatoid arthritis at 15 years of age.
Reading: The arthritis was caused by exposure to chemicals between 8 and 14 years of age.

F 51 yrs 11-12-99
Problem: She has had emotional problems for the past 3 years and cries a lot. She has trouble getting small tasks done, has gained weight, and is tired all the time. She has tried using herbs, but they do not seem to work. She does not sleep well.
Reading: Her brain tissue looks irritated, probably from some type of chemical or medication exposure. She has strong energy blockage in both sides of her body. It looks like two dark, long rods that start at the front base of the neck and run down through both lungs and into the outer portion of the digestive area. She should be treated for a chemical exposure. Although her symptoms appear to be caused by emotions, they are physical.

F 48 yrs 03-14-99
Problem: She has shooting pains throughout her body. An MRI has

revealed four bulging disks in her neck. Doctors say that her spinal canal is too narrow (spinal stenosis) and pinching a nerve.

Reading: She has been exposed to chemicals that have spread to or affected the brain. (She then stated that she worked in a plastics factory.) The most affected area is from the side of the head down into the back of the skull. The spinal fluid pressure is causing nerve disruption. The four disks in the neck may have ruptured because of the spinal fluid pressure, or there may be no real rupture; just spinal fluid pressure might be causing the disks to bulge. She needs to see a neurologist and a naturopath. She should drink plenty of water and liquid vegetables to help detoxify her body. She should use a sauna three to four times a week for 2 weeks and avoid chemical irritants (e.g., perfume) or hair products before the sauna. She also should avoid dying her hair for 60 days. It would be okay for her to use products with a natural base, however.

M 48 yrs 06-29-99

Problem: He has red spots all over his body that come and go but mostly stay. For the last 10 years he has had extremely dry feet, and his toenails are yellow and thickened. His prostate gland is a concern as well. His urination is slow, and his semen is scant. These symptoms also began 9 to 10 years ago. One doctor told him that he has a blockage in the prostate, and another said his problems are based on emotions.

Reading: He does not have a blockage in the prostate, but rather a narrowing. His body tissues are dry and lack elasticity, which could be part of the prostate problem. The tubes or veins to the prostate area are more problematic than the prostate itself. This might have originated from an exposure to chemicals. (He then revealed that he worked with many chemicals 10 years ago.) He should try both reflexology and acupuncture. The skin spots are related to the chemical reactions from 10 years ago. He needs to keep his skin very clean and well lubricated.

F 42 yrs 11-03-99

Problem: She was diagnosed with fibromyalgia 15 years ago. An MRI has shown noncancerous tumors near the pelvic bones. She has spastic hip joints and chronic leg and ankle pain. She is always tired. She has been to several doctors, but no one has determined a cause.

Reading: Most of her pain is physical, not emotional. She should see a nephrologist to look at her kidneys. This is a partial reason for her illness. Her body reacted to an exposure to chemicals. (She then stated that when she was 21 years of age she was exposed to film processing chemicals and her facial skin broke out in boils.) She needs her liver and pancreas treated with acupuncture and herbs. Her kidneys were the first organs to feel the effects of the chemicals. She will see a 60% improvement over the next 2 to 3 years.

F 53 yrs 08-19-00

Problem: She wants to know if she has cancer.

Reading: She does not have cancer. She has patches of toxic blockage throughout her body. This is not energy blockage; this is toxic buildup. The blockage is in the lower neck, parts of both breasts, rib area, gallbladder, pancreas, and appendix. Her body has become toxic during the last 10 or 12 years. She is very sensitive to chemicals. She should avoid pesticide spray, pool supplies, etc. She needs to detoxify her blood and sweat and use herbs to flush her gallbladder, pancreas, and blood. She should try acupuncture and reflexology and see a naturopath for the detoxifying herbs.

F 49 yrs 10-17-96

Problem: She has had diarrhea and constipation for 18 months, as well as pain in her digestive system and colon area. She takes colonic enemas. She also has a form of skin cancer.

Reading: Her stomach might be having a toxic reaction caused by pesticide spray, dish soap, and laundry detergents. This reaction might even be airborne, and the heavy pollution might be a problem. She needs to avoid chemicals as well as pools and spas because of the chlorine. She has a blockage in the upper portion of the colon. This problem is most likely related to toxins as well, as are the constipation and abdominal pain. Her liver is slightly toxic, too. She wears a little too much makeup, which could be toxic or irritating to her skin. She needs to use less deodorant and perfume because they could be toxic to her. She might change the brand or use a natural deodorant. The overall toxic buildup might get worse if she does not get it under control. She should stop taking the colonics because they might be slightly irritating to her stomach and are not helping anyway. She might try taking saunas to sweat out the toxins in her body. She needs to be sure that her clothes, bedclothes, and dishes are rinsed well. She should drink purified water and breathe clean air. After making these changes, this problem will get much better, and she should respond positively.

M 14 yrs 02-08-98

Problem: He was diagnosed with a condition involving internal hemorrhaging of the colon when he was 5 years of age. This disorder can affect the kidneys and other organs when he gets older.

Reading: His colon is enlarged and continually irritated; therefore it is very sensitive to pesticides and environmental pollution. Although he needs to avoid carbonated and citrus drinks, he will become sick much more quickly with what he breathes than with what he eats. His family should avoid pesticides sprayed inside the home and chlorine in concentrated amounts in the water. He will suffer stomach problems when he is an adult. Of all the chemicals, pesticides would be the worst. His lungs are very sensitive to chemicals and could easily be affected. This needs to be closely monitored. Inflammation is already present in the lower portion of both lungs. He should bathe with a natural, nonchemical soap.

F 41 yrs 11-03-98

Problem: She is concerned about getting skin cancer because her sister died of it at 24 years of age.

Reading: Her state of mind is very important regarding whether she will get skin cancer. Her skin is at risk most with exposure to pesticides, followed by exposure to the sun. Chlorine is a factor as well. She should avoid outdoor Jacuzzis and watch free radicals (formed in connection with, for example, sunlight and environmental irritants such as smoke and air pollution). She should read up on and take selenium, a trace mineral that protects the skin at the cellular level from damage caused by free radicals.

F 49 yrs 12-13-99
Problem: She had skin cancer removed from her legs.
Reading: Her skin is very sensitive to chemicals, and her blood is toxic. Her condition will change if she detoxifies her blood. Eating by her blood type would also help this problem.

F 48 yrs 01-14-01
Problem: She has a history of skin cancer in four different areas.
Reading: Her skin is chemically sensitive, perhaps to laundry detergent and pool chemicals. She needs to avoid alcohol and take selenium to help eliminate free radicals from her skin.

F 57 yrs 02-20-01
Problem: She has wheat intolerance, among other food sensitivities. Diagnostic tests have shown that she has high, toxic levels of metals in her system.
Reading: The back, upper portion of her brain has been exposed to chemicals, most likely oil-based chemicals and lead. (She then stated that she is an artist.) These likely are the metals showing up as toxic levels in her system. The wheat intolerance is a result of this chemical exposure. She should see a naturopathic physician for herbs that would cleanse her system of these metals.

F 57 yrs 04-22-01
Problem: She had a bacterial infection to the face 5 years ago for which she took antibiotics and cortisone, but it did not clear up completely. Acidic foods cause it to flare up, and she has had open lesions.
Reading: This is not an infection. She apparently has the same condition on her lower arms and hands. This is occurring because of an airborne pollutant that is causing her blood to be toxic. (She then said that she is a hair stylist and breathes chemicals every day.) Her thymus

gland is a problem because it is allowing high levels of toxins to enter her body, and her lungs are a secondary problem because they cannot filter the toxins. Nerves and stress trigger an even greater flare-up. Her thymus gland needs to be stimulated to enhance its functioning capabilities.

F 63 yrs 05-28-01
Problem: For the past 6 years she has experienced pain and dizziness while walking or climbing stairs. The pain can be in different parts of her body, although the pain in the base of her neck is fairly consistent. She has to hold her hands around her neck until the pain goes away.
Reading: This is a blood disorder from an exposure to chemicals— probably a food pesticide. It has affected her pituitary gland, which releases chemical toxins into the bloodstream and lymphatic system, particularly in the neck. Her pancreas is toxic as well. The thymus gland is affected and needs to be stimulated and detoxified. She needs to detoxify the blood through a change of diet, and the glands and organs need reflexology and acupuncture.

CHEST PAIN/DISCOMFORT

F 43 yrs 02-21-99
Problem: She has chest pains when exercising.
Reading: The chest pains are stress-related and from a lack of potassium. Acupuncture could help the stress level.

F 59 yrs 01-11-99
Problem: She has chest pain, chest pressure, and heart palpitations. She had colon surgery 2 years ago.

Reading: She never fully recovered from colon surgery, either physically or emotionally. The chest pain is an emotional response to her anticipation of physical pain. She has anxiety attacks from this as well. When she experiences pain she should slow down and work through it.

F 58 yrs 05-08-00

Problem: She has chest tightness. She is scheduled for a stress test on her heart.

Reading: She looks very alone, afraid, and disappointed, and she is struggling emotionally. Her emotional side is causing most of her physical problems. She has a very minor two-artery blockage, but it will not result in an operation. She has energy blockage in the chest, heart, and upper stomach for which she needs acupuncture and other energy work.

M 53 yrs 04-24-00

Problem: He has had three stents placed in his coronary artery but still suffers from mild chest pain. Tests are negative, and doctors say it is indigestion.

Reading: His chest pain is coming from the back side of his heart. The problem is too much cholesterol in his blood. The source of the problem is probably the pancreas, which is not functioning normally and is contributing to the cholesterol problem. About 60% of the cause of the abnormally functioning pancreas is stress.

F 58 yrs 02-21-00

Problem: She has had a jabbing pain in the upper left side of her chest for the last 2 weeks. Her neck and shoulders have been painful and stiff as well.

Reading: The pain in her chest is the result of tight trapezius muscles, as is the pain in her neck and shoulders. This is both stress-related and from a lack of exercise. She needs yoga for mind and body connection.

M 55 yrs 01-28-98

Problem: He has had recent chest discomfort and is concerned about his heart.

Reading: His heart is okay. The problem lies behind the heart or chest area. He has digestive problems, heartburn, and obesity. He has a lining of fat around his heart, but it has not yet affected the heart. He needs to cut back on caffeine. The caffeine is stimulating his heart and contributing to a narrowing of the arteries, which is speeding up his heartbeat. The acid in citrus fruits and caffeine beverages is contributing to the heartburn.

M 74 yrs 06-04-01

Problem: He has had mild chest pain over the sternum for 8 years. Recent tests show nothing wrong with his heart, but an ECG has revealed that something may be wrong with a heart valve. He is very short of breath when he climbs stairs, and his blood pressure is low. The toes on both of his feet are numb. His brain tells him that his toes are cold, but when he touches them they are warm. Numerous tests have been negative. He also has a hiatal hernia and acid reflux, which has burned his lower esophagus.

Reading: His hypothalamus is misfiring and gives the impression of having convulsions. It is affecting the nervous system and his entire body. His heart valve in the upper ventricle is not leaky, but it is sticky. It opens and closes slowly, particularly when opening. This problem and the shortness of breath are most likely connected to the hypothalamus. The valve needs stimulation either with traditional or natural medication, acupuncture, and minerals such as potassium. The hypothalamus also needs treatment to get it back in rhythm. Impaired circulation to his lower extremities and his esophageal problems are tied to the nervous disorder caused by his hypothalamus gland.

CHILLS

M 38 yrs 11-30-98
Problem: He has night chills.
Reading: The night chills are a blood pressure related condition. His blood pressure drops while he is asleep, causing the chills. He needs to stimulate the thymus gland with a supplement to help control the night chills.

M 84 yrs 01-24-00
Problem: He has chills and a tingling throughout his body usually in the morning, but it can occur at anytime. All medical tests have come back negative.
Reading: This appears to be blood-pressure–related. The aorta looks weak, and when he is resting it does not have the strength to pump his blood normally. He needs to lie on a recline board (his head lower than his feet) for 10 to 20 minutes in the morning and at night, 7 days a week. He should do push-ups (keeping his knees on the floor), as many as he is comfortable doing, to help strengthen the aorta, and he should take apple cider vinegar for potassium. Symptoms should then subside.

M 50 yrs 06-19-00
Problem: He has periodic cold chills. Recently he had a benign tumor on his thyroid gland.
Reading: The cold chills are linked to the thyroid problem, which developed because of toxins in his blood. He needs energy work on his thyroid gland.

F 41 yrs 06-29-99
Problem: She feels chilled or cold all the time.
Reading: When she gets chilled, it is caused by a very quick drop in energy. A food supplement, optimally a carbohydrate, would raise her energy level to normal and stop the chills.

F 65 yrs 03-03-01
Problem: She has had chills, headaches, and dizziness for 2 years. Three chiropractors have been unable to tell her the cause.
Reading: Hormones from her adrenal gland are low, and when she moves quickly or becomes tired she gets dizzy. This is also the reason for her headaches and chills. The adrenal gland should be treated with acupuncture and herbs. After about 60 days of this treatment, her hormone levels should be checked. If they are still low, she should begin use of an adrenal hormone.

M 50 yrs 05-21-01
Problem: He experiences chills, and his temperature drops to 96° F at times. He was diagnosed with depression 15 years ago and has been off and on medication since then. At times medication does not help. He has lost his zest for life and wants to know why he is experiencing these problems.
Reading: The chills are caused by deficient hormonal release from the pituitary gland. The left side of his brain, the center of the brain, and the pituitary gland are not getting energy. Something is pressing on them, and normal chemical releases in the brain are not occurring. As a result he is also tired and depressed and cannot think clearly. Acupuncture and perhaps electrical stimulation to these areas would help, as well as nutritional herbs that help brain function. He is low in minerals, particularly zinc, potassium, and magnesium. Because oxygen and blood flow are decreased to the left side of his brain, he should sleep on his right side to minimize the pressure to the left side.

CHOLESTEROL, INCREASED

F 49 yrs 12-13-99
Problem: She is concerned that her high cholesterol level is affecting her heart.
Reading: She is a strong candidate for eating by her blood type. The blood-type diet should help control her high cholesterol levels.

F 54 yrs 11-24-98
Problem: She has high cholesterol.
Reading: Her cholesterol problem is partly hereditary and partly dietary. Her stress level is a factor as well. She should eat according to her blood type. Her gallbladder looks slightly toxic and has a buildup of fat. Her hearing is okay but not great; she has an equal loss in both ears. A change of diet will keep the hearing loss from getting worse. Her high cholesterol level has not helped her hearing.

M 46 yrs 11-03-99
Problem: He has high cholesterol.
Reading: His diet is not compatible with his blood type, and this is causing the high cholesterol level.

F 45 yrs 12-10-00
Problem: She has circulatory problems and leg and vein discomfort.
Reading: High cholesterol is the issue with her circulation, leg, and vein problems. Eating according to her blood type would help her.

F 52 yrs 06-02-01
Problem: She has high cholesterol and is under a lot of family stress.

Reading: Her adrenal glands are 50% depleted as a result of stress and are raising her cholesterol level.

F 69 yrs 08-04-01
Problem: She has high cholesterol but believes that her medication has it under control.
Reading: She is not in the clear with her cholesterol. Her pancreas is the cause of her cholesterol problems. Acupuncture and reflexology to the pancreas would help keep her cholesterol under control.

CHRONIC FATIGUE

F 59 yrs 03-07-98
Problem: She has chronic fatigue. She claims to be "allergic" to everything, including electricity.
Reading: She has an energy blockage that runs through the front part of the brain between the eyes and down through the back of the throat to the base of her neck. This blockage has interfered with her brain's attempt to process the information that she receives visually. Inasmuch as the right eye controls the left side of the brain and the left eye controls the right side of the brain, the interference is right where this switch, or crisscross, takes place behind the eyes. This is a cause of the chronic fatigue, why exposure to electricity, computers, and fluorescent lighting bothers her, and why she has trouble focusing her thoughts. The energy blockage is most likely interfering with the nerves and mucous membranes that should be flowing naturally but cannot. She needs energy work, possibly even by hand in some of the areas that are difficult to treat such as the brain, and acupuncture in the other areas.

M 44 yrs 01-08-01

Problem: He has chronic fatigue. He was first diagnosed 15 years ago and suffered a relapse 6 months ago. At that time he received an injection in his left arm for the chronic fatigue and ever since he has experienced severe pain in that arm and chest and has been having frequent colds.

Reading: The soft tissue in his neck and throat—most likely lymphatic—has been affected, and this is the reason for his health problems and the cause of the chronic fatigue syndrome. He has an energy blockage in his neck that needs energy work, and this will help the lymphatic system drain. He holds stress in his neck as well. The sides of his brain are also a concern because the fatigue syndrome has affected these areas. The virus is dormant in his body and activated at times by the energy blockage to the lymphatic tissue in the neck. His organs look okay but would look better if not for the viral infection.

M 42 yrs 02-12-01

Problem: He has chronic fatigue. Doctors have been unable to identify the cause or cure. He has been receiving vitamin B_{12} injections and antiseizure medications to help him sleep. He wakes up very tired with muscle and joint pain.

Reading: The first vertebra in his neck is locked down, driving pain straight down his spine. His head appears to be tilted back, lifting his chin up. His jaw joint is very tight, and there is pressure on his brain. (He then stated that he gets headaches in the back of his head and off to the left side.) Vitamin B_{12} injections and antiseizure medication will not help him. First he needs Rolfing to the neck and then to the back of the head, followed by the jaw joint. Then he needs acupuncture to open the energy to the jaw, cheeks, and bottom teeth. The swelling in the brain looks medicine-related. (He then stated that he overdosed on aspirin when he was a child.)

M 36 yrs 02-24-01

Problem: He was diagnosed with chronic fatigue in his twenties. He gets so tired that he cannot make it through a workday without lying down. He also suffers from paranoia and social anxiety and believes that he has a brain disorder.

Reading: His brain looks clear, but he has an infection or disorder of the blood in the spinal cord at the base of his head and neck that appears to be multiple sclerosis. It seems to be in the dura mater. (He confirmed that his spine is very sensitive.) He needs to have the WBCs and RBCs of his blood checked and a spinal tap to assess his spinal fluid. He may have had meningitis when he was in his early twenties.

F 40 yrs 04-21-01

Problem: She has been ill for the past 20 years with headaches, bloating, constipation, diarrhea, and other digestive problems. She became bedridden 3 years ago and has no energy to get out of bed. Her only diagnosis has been chronic fatigue, and she wants to know what is causing her problems.

Reading: Her brain has shifted or slid backward from the forehead and is resting on the back portion of her head. As a result her entire body and all her organs are functioning extremely slowly because of this pressure on the brain. She should lie face down with a pillow or two under her chest and drop her head forward. Cranial massage may enable the cranium and, even more critically, the brain to move forward. She must also increase oxygen flow to the capillaries and blood vessels of her brain. Energy work would move energy to the upper back portion of her shoulders, up through her neck and head, and out through the top of her head.

CIRCULATORY PROBLEMS

F 56 yrs 03-13-00
Reading: She has circulatory problems. The heart and lungs look weak, which has created the weak blood flow throughout her body. She needs cardiovascular exercise. Apple cider vinegar would also help her heart and lungs.

F 66 yrs 03-19-98
Problem: Her right leg vein protrudes between the ankle and mid-calf area. When she takes her weight off the leg, the vein reduces in size. She also gets shooting pains up the leg to the groin. Lying down and elevating her legs helps the pain. Doctors do not know what is causing the vein to react this way.
Reading: She has a problem with circulation. Blood is not adequately getting through from the upper half of the body to the lower half. The main artery in the neck, which is responsible for transferring blood to the heart and ultimately sending it to the groin area, is not properly functioning, resulting in a limited blood supply. This lack of blood to the groin and lower legs causes poor functioning of the muscles in the lower leg. When the vein in the lower leg tries to pump blood back up through the leg, she does not have an adequate supply of blood and oxygen to accomplish this task. Therefore blood remains in the lower half of the leg. The pain occurs when the vein attempts to send the blood upward but cannot. The blood circulates better once it reaches the upper half of her body. Lying down to lessen the pain would make sense, because the vein does not have to work as hard in that position. She needs to have the main vein or artery in the neck checked, as well

as those in her heart, groin, and leg. Although this is not serious, it is the main cause of her problem.

F 40 yrs 08-27-99
Problem: She wants a general reading.
Reading: She is in the very early stages of having lower leg circulatory problems, starting in the ankles and progressing upward. The blood has a more difficult time traveling from the ankles. A lack of exercise causes this condition. She needs to begin an exercise program that includes running, cycling, walking, or swimming. If she does not do this, the condition will get worse and her ankles will begin to swell. She should lie on a recline board (her head lower than her legs) 20 minutes per day.

F 7 yrs 03-07-00
Reading: She has chronic stomach pain and constipation. She has been on herbs for a month with little results. An abdominal x-ray examination was negative.
Reading: The heart is not sending normal amounts of blood to the digestive area, which in turn is causing the digestive disorder and constipation. She likely becomes tired quickly or easily and perhaps even experiences shortness of breath from time to time. She also appears to be experiencing muscle aches in the thighs as a result of the lack of circulation. Her mother confirmed that the patient had a heart murmur at 2 years of age. She needs medical follow-up for this problem.

F 45 yrs 12-10-00
Problem: She has circulatory problems and leg and vein discomfort.
Reading: High cholesterol is the issue with her circulation, leg, and vein problems. Eating according to her blood type would help her.

F 75 yrs 11-27-00
Problem: She was diagnosed with circulatory problems as the cause of her calf pain.
Reading: Her organs all look good, as does her circulation. The pain in

her calf is coming from arthritis in her lower lumbar region. The pain increases when she is sitting for too long.

F 63 yrs 01-29-01
Problem: She has poor circulation in her legs.
Reading: She has too much fat in her blood, which is causing gout and affecting her spleen. Her spleen is full of toxins and fat, and this is causing her circulatory problems. She needs almost all mineral supplements as well as energy work from the spleen up through her chest, neck, and face.

F 82 yrs 04-16-01
Problem: She has arthritis in the knees and feet, itching on the back, and circulation problems in the left leg. Her chiropractor has told her that she has fibrous tissue adjacent to her colon that is cutting off circulation in her leg and foot. He has worked on these areas for the past 8 years but with little improvement.
Reading: Her blood has become toxic because her liver, pancreas, and gallbladder have not been filtering properly. Acupuncture to these organs would open them up and improve their filtering capabilities. This is the cause of her poor leg circulation, arthritis, and itching on her back. Eating according to her blood type would also improve her blood.

CONSTIPATION

F 59 yrs 12-21-98
Problem: She has long-term constipation and diarrhea. Doctors have been unable to determine what is wrong with her colon. At one time she did not have a bowel movement for 3 months. Herbs give her

diarrhea, and she never knows if she is going to have constipation or diarrhea.

Reading: Most of her problem is in the stomach, surrounding organs, and colon. This is mostly a nerve interference problem. She needs to see a chiropractor for an adjustment of a vertebra in her back just above the kidneys. She also needs Rolfing and reflexology. These practitioners should concentrate on the stomach, gallbladder, spleen, liver, and other organs before they begin work on the colon. They need to avoid the upper colon until some of the tenderness leaves this area. The Rolfing and reflexology will give her a 30% improvement. After 30 days of Rolfing and reflexology she should then see a psychotherapist. She has a lot of energy blockage in the stomach and midsection that is caused by emotions. She wants to avoid the emotional aspect, but it cannot be avoided. She also needs to drink plenty of water.

M 43 yrs 05-18-97
Problem: He has had life-long constipation.
Reading: He needs to improve his diet with supplements and detoxify his body with steam baths or saunas. He should drink three times the amount of water that he currently drinks to help eliminate the toxins and prevent constipation.

F 55 yrs 04-20-99
Problem: She has chronic constipation for which she has tried herbs, but they have not helped.
Reading: The constipation may be linked to allergies or chemicals. She has energy blockage to the front half of her body, starting at the pubic area and traveling upward to her neck. The entire digestive area is blocked, which is why she has difficulty digesting and is constipated. She needs energy work, reflexology, acupuncture, relaxation (e.g., yoga), and a lot of liquids. She fights the emotional side of herself and likely will continue to shut down her energy. Optimally the acupuncture will help keep her energy open.

F 51 yrs 09-13-99

Problem: She has constipation and a sleeping disorder for which she is taking sleeping pills. She is paralyzed from a car accident and is in a care facility.

Reading: The colon moves and processes foods well, but this process is drastically slowed down in the small intestine. She should be moved in bed every 30 minutes rather than the current 3 hours. Nurses should massage her stomach and exercise her legs in an upward motion toward the stomach. This movement will help the small intestine become more active. She should also be taken off the sleeping pills. They are not really helping her sleep and are contributing to her constipation.

F 48 yrs 09-13-99

Problem: She has been constipated since having had a colonic enema a month ago.

Reading: She has an energy blockage to her entire digestive tract, mostly caused by emotion. She needs energy work from the knees up through the top of the head on the front side only, concentrating on the digestive area. She tries too hard to be successful and is always looking for ways to improve herself, including in her marriage. Nothing is good enough for her, and this attitude needs to stop if she is to be well. She is also taking too many natural vitamins and minerals and needs to avoid these products for a while.

F 75 yrs 11-27-00

Problem: She has constipation.

Reading: She has blocked energy starting from the eyes to the descending colon. Acupuncture will help this. She should also watch salt intake, increase dietary oils, and stop eating bread.

F 71 yrs 07-07-01

Problem: She has had constipation and bloating all her adult life. Recent acupuncture and herbal treatments have helped somewhat, but both the chiropractor and naturopath believe that her problem is emotional.

Reading: The constipation is caused by a lack of minerals that are necessary for digestion. Her digestive problems are not caused by her emotional state. The naturopath might give her minerals such as selenium and lipids such as lecithin. The chiropractor can treat her digestive tract with acupuncture, but until she increases her minerals she will not have the relief she seeks.

COUGH, CHRONIC

F 73 yrs 09-05-99
Problem: She has had chronic cough for 30 years for which she is seeing an allergist, but she has not been helped.
Reading: She needs to pay more attention to her diet by watching her fat and salt intake. Her cough is food-sensitivity related, mainly to sugar and salt. She might try sipping on hot honey lemon water. She needs to be tested for food sensitivities.

F 52 yrs 12-13-98
Problem: She has recurrent cough, which she believes is caused by a wood-burning fireplace.
Reading: She has allergies and coughs because her throat is overly sensitive and quick to become irritated. Pollens bother her throat and upper respiratory area. Fireplaces are contributing to the coughing. She should try a room air humidifier.

M 46 yrs 01-25-99
Problem: He has a dry, chronic cough. He also uses one can of chewing tobacco per day.
Reading: The cough is linked to a sinus condition (60%) and to the nicotine in the tobacco (40%).

DEPRESSION

F 57 yrs 11-24-98
Problem: She has depression, anxiety attacks, and a history of mental breakdowns. She has been on most types of mental drugs and herbs with no effect. The drug that she is on now affects her thinking process and memory. She does not have a good self-image and has threatened others who are weaker than she is. She has been divorced twice.
Reading: She has a strong fear of being alone. She needs to listen to positive reinforcement tapes daily, and see a hypnotherapist for regression therapy once a week. The top of her head has energy blockage. A practitioner such as a naturopath should perform energy work and find the proper herbs for her.

F 31 yrs 06-02-00
Problem: She has had depression since a close friend died 5 months ago. She wants to know if she has a chemical imbalance.
Reading: Medication, yoga, tai chi, and acupuncture would all help. She should take the medication for 3 to 6 months until she is more focused and then switch to the alternative treatments. She does not believe that she has accomplished enough in both her personal life and work. She needs to fix the work issue first; she wastes too much time during the day. She is also slightly sensitive to an environmental chemical, which has affected her head. She might take saunas.

M 62 yrs 09-28-99
Problem: He has depression and a bipolar condition for which he is on many strong medications. In the last 3 weeks he has gained 20 pounds

and cannot put his shoes on because of the fluid buildup in his legs. He has become constipated as well.

Reading: His main physical problem is his kidneys. They are the primary cause of the water retention. This is occurring because his medications are too strong. He needs to see a naturopath for St. John's Wort and other herbs, which would enable him to wean off his antidepression medications. Acupuncture would also help with the depression. Constipation will subside when he decreases or eliminates the medications.

F 62 yrs 08-05-99

Problem: She has had depression since she was 4 years of age; it can last for as long as a year at a time. She was sexually molested and had many fears as a child. She has spent several years in a mental institution and was an alcoholic until 9 years ago.

Reading: She has a lot of energy blockage in her face. She has a deep yearning to be held and loved, and she cannot get enough of either and never will. She needs energy work, reflexology, and psychotherapy.

M 46 yrs 01-25-99

Problem: A large drum fell on him in an industrial accident, and he was told that he would never leave a wheelchair. He is depressed about his physical condition and being out of shape.

Reading: He is very intelligent and needs to take an interest in himself, exercise, and challenge his mind by reading. Yoga or tai chi would be good for relaxation.

F 23 yrs 02-26-98

Problem: She has been depressed for 6 weeks and has been withdrawn from her husband. She also has low energy and is not sleeping well.

Reading: Her level of depression is mild, but it will lake a lot of work and time to overcome it–6 to 18 months. Her problem is a lack of energy flow. The top center of her head is blocked, and energy is not getting through. This is an important factor and needs to be corrected. Once the energy problem is fixed, she will see a major change. Her body is not breathing. She needs to meditate and do mild exercises (e.g., yoga or tai chi) but avoid heavy exercises. She should shorten her school hours, not her work hours, and listen more to music that stimulates her. She is not analytical, but she dwells on her thoughts too much. She should avoid having too much quiet time. She should not avoid her husband. He is an important element in her life and a significant piece of the puzzle in getting emotionally well. She will begin to come around to her husband within the next 6 months. He cares about her very much, and she should force herself to become more affectionate and sexually involved with him. They could take short trips together. They will grow and have a strong future together.

F 45 yrs 04-25-99

Problem: She has long-term depression and mood swings. Doctors want to test her brain.

Reading: The problem is a combination of energy blockage and nerve disorder in the brain. Her pituitary gland is healthy, but it is being affected by the blockage and will restore once the energy is opened. First she had the nerve disorder because of stress, and then it shut down her energy. Initially she needs energy work, including reflexology. A natural herb might help her temperament.

F 42 yrs 08-27-99

Problem: She is depressed and has had pelvic, hip, and abdominal pain for the last 8 months.

Reading: The pain is blood-related, not skeletal. She has pain and pressure in the front of her face, and her eyes are dark and burn. The blood appears to have a virus or infection that has settled in her lower torso area but runs up through the center of her chest and throughout the body. She should see a naturopath to treat her blood and digestive disorder with herbs, which will improve her enzymes. Her depression will improve by 70% if the physical problem is corrected. Acupuncture to her face also will help the depression.

F 44 yrs 10-11-99

Problem: She has had life-long depression. Therapy and antidepression medications have not helped. She cries easily and cannot handle criticism. She also has low energy.

Reading: Her depression began when she was around 3 years of age because of loneliness. The back of her head, which has had blocked energy since she was 3, needs energy work. She has spent her life wondering why she is depressed. The only absolute reason is that she has always felt alone and still does. She needs to see a therapist who will help her cope with her loneliness. Her smoking contributes negatively to her depression. Depression is the source of her low energy as well.

M 54 yrs 11-26-99

Problem: He is taking medication for depression. He has low blood pressure, stomach ulcers, and body pain.

Reading: He is depleted of minerals. His kidneys are failing because his adrenal glands are depleted, and his adrenal glands are depleted because of a lack of minerals. The medication he is taking for depression is having a negative affect on his adrenal glands. He should be on a natural herb for his depression, and his urine should be tested to confirm mineral loss.

F 68 yrs 12-10-99

Problem: She has depression and anxiety.

Reading: She has severe mineral deficiency, particularly of zinc and potassium. She also has heavy energy blockage to the chest.

F 55 yrs 04-10-00

Problem: She has had life-long depression and post-polio syndrome.

Reading: She has current issues affecting her emotionally that need to be dealt with before dealing with her childhood issues. She needs energy work in her chest and lower neck and to see an acupuncturist for depression. She needs at least a 40% improvement in her depression, which will help the post-polio problems. She should rely less on doctors and medications and learn to care for herself a little more. However, she will likely not get behind these challenges.

M 48 yrs 07-12-99

Problem: He has depression and anxiety. A psychiatrist put him on an antidepressant.

Reading: The antidepression medication has not had much of an effect. St. John's Wort would be more helpful. He is worried about depression and anxiety, and his mind appears to be slightly detached from his body. He might try yoga or tai chi.

F 38 yrs 09-25-00

Problem: Her depression has lasted off and on for years. At times she has to force herself to leave her house. She has been off medication for 8 months and is doing fine without it.

Reading: An energy block over the front of her face is causing this depression, and her pituitary gland is weak. Acupuncture would help her.

M 45 yrs 12-31-00

Problem: He has major depression.

Reading: He is clinically depressed. He fits the definition of depression, but he should avoid medication. Acupuncture, hypnotherapy, Rolfing, and reflexology will help him improve about 60%. First he should have three acupuncture and hypnotherapy treatments, followed by Rolfing (he is the first client for which I have suggested this treatment for depression), and then reflexology. He will need a series of four treatments a year just to maintain a 60% improvement.

M 59 yrs 02-05-01

Problem: He was diagnosed with bipolar disorder. He was adopted at 2 years of age.

Reading: The center of his head (the "soft spot" in newborns) is the main cause of his bipolar condition or nerve disorder. A nerve in this area zigzags outward to the top edge of his head and downward across both eyes into the upper cheeks. His condition is mild. Treatment by acupuncture to the top of his head will help him improve.

F 19 yrs 05-12-01

Problem: She was in a psychiatric ward for 3 weeks with manic-depression, bipolar disorder, brain chemical disorder, and hypersexual behavior. Her father says that she was a good student until she was 15 years of age when she got into drugs and became depressed.

Reading: Her problems began when she was a young child between 5 and 8 years of age. She has an "A-frame" shape to the energy in her head and brain. The center of her brain is not functioning properly because the energy at the exterior areas squeezes it. This energy needs to be flattened so that all of the brain receives the energy, not just the exterior portions. She probably complains of pressure inside her head. She had a lot of energy–perhaps too much–as a young child and was happy-go-lucky. Then her life slowly began to change. Energy needs to be moved from the top of her head downward through the neck, shoulders, arms, and out through her hands. If her energy improves, then her medication can be reduced. Her energy needs to be restored and balanced to the way it was when she was 5 years of age. (Her father said that her cat died when she was 7, and she has commented since then that everyone leaves her.) The energy blockage to the brain was triggered by an emotional event, probably the death of the pet. (Her father also confirms that she was happy and full of energy as a young child.)

M 50 yrs 05-21-01

Problem: He was diagnosed with depression 15 years ago and has been on and off medication since then. At times medication does not help. He also experiences chills, and his temperature drops to 96° F. He has lost his zest for life and wants to know why he is experiencing these problems.

Reading: The left side of his brain, the center of the brain, and the pituitary gland are not getting energy. Something is pressing on them, and the normal chemical releases in the brain are not occurring. As a result he is tired and depressed and cannot think clearly. The chills are caused by insufficient hormonal release from the pituitary gland. Acupuncture and perhaps electrical stimulation to these areas would help, as well as nutritional herbs that help brain function. He is also low in minerals, particularly zinc, potassium, and magnesium, and oxygen and blood flow to the left side of his brain are decreased. He should sleep on his right side to minimize pressure to the left side of his brain. This depression can improve with treatment.

F 20 yrs 07-02-01

Problem: She has been battling depression since she was 10 years of age. She dropped out of school at 13 years of age. She has attempted suicide and began having panic attacks at 16 years of age and did not leave the house for a year. She is now trying to socialize again and finish school, but she gets dizzy, sleeps a lot, and has short-term memory loss. She is taking an antidepressant.

Reading: She wanted everything to be perfect, including her parents' marriage. Her depression at 10 years of age was really an attitude or behavior to try to keep them together. She is neither clinically nor chemically depressed, and her problem is fixable. She has an energy blockage to the throat, thyroid gland, thymus gland, lungs, and reproductive area. Acupuncture to these blocked areas and discontinuation of the antidepressant would improve her energy and fatigue. In addition, she should have psychological and behavioral treatments as follows: (1) positive reinforcement tapes and psychotherapy to change her behavior; (2) acupuncture treatments to the energy-blocked areas; (3) daily reflexology; and (4) physical exercises such as yoga, martial arts, or tai chi.

F 57 yrs 05-27-01

Problem: She was diagnosed with depression 9 years ago, and she believes that it is hereditary. She is taking both traditional and homeopathic medications. Recently her bowel movements have changed. She also has had right-sided chest pain that has come and gone for 3 years.

Reading: Mixing traditional and homeopathic antidepression medications is not a good idea for her. She needs one or the other, and the natural type would be better for a while. The traditional medication, separately and together with the homeopathic medication, is upsetting the good bacteria in her digestive tract and causing toxin buildup in her blood, resulting in the bowel changes she is experiencing. However, her depression is manageable. She is not seriously depressed, but because she believes that she is, she is resigned to staying depressed. The traditional medicine is also causing the chest pains. She should take apple cider vinegar to help clear her blood of the toxins and promote energy.

M 39 yrs 08-15-01

Problem: He was diagnosed 3 years ago with obsessive-compulsive disorder, for which doctors have prescribed an antidepressant. He becomes nervous and anxious when he is not on the medication, and he has not worked for the past 10 months.

Reading: He does not have a brain dysfunction. His lungs have absorbed poisons and carbon monoxide, and these toxins have poisoned his blood. (He works at an airport loading and unloading airplanes and is exposed to airborne carbons.) His poor lung quality and shallow breathing give him the sensation of suffocation, which adds to his anxiety. His obsessive-compulsiveness comes about because of his fear that stems from his poor health and would improve when his health improves. He needs to cleanse his blood, lungs, and liver of toxins with herbs, pure oxygen or good air, saunas for sweating and opening up his pores, and plenty of purified drinking water. Acupuncture to the diaphragm, lung, liver, and thymus gland would help as well. These treatments will help him more than the antidepressant. After he improves his health, he could use a few psychotherapy sessions to help him get refocused.

DIABETES

F 43 yrs 11-02-98
Problem: She has chronic bone and joint pain, weight gain, and stomach and gallbladder problems. She is concerned about becoming diabetic.
Reading: The bone and joint pain is related to her high blood sugar level, which is also causing the digestive problems. She is very close to becoming diabetic.

F 49 yrs 12-13-99
Problem: She requested a general reading.
Reading: She is a strong candidate for eating according to her blood type. Her pancreas has been most affected by her diet. She is susceptible to diabetes. The blood-type diet should help prevent diabetes from occurring.

F 46 yrs 12-29-99
Problem: She was diagnosed with diabetes. She cannot get motivated to exercise, and she also feels stressed. Recently she had surgery for pre-cancerous cells in her cervix.
Reading: Her diabetes is highly stress-related. Eating by her blood type would be very important, along with stress reduction. She can prevent the diabetes from getting worse. If she does not, she will become insulin dependent and require more surgery.

F 61 yrs 02-11-01
Problem: She has diabetes. She does not yet take insulin injections.
Reading: She needs energy work through her pancreas to avoid having to have insulin injections. Acupuncture and reflexology would be good.

M 58 yrs 05-07-01

Problem: He was diagnosed with diabetes 8 years ago. He says it robs him of his energy and sex drive, and he has a difficult time keeping his blood sugar under control.

Reading: His diabetes is not quite the hindrance he thinks it is. The lymphatic glands high up in his neck are swelling and may be pressuring the thyroid gland. Also, his energy is shut down at the navel, which is affecting his sex organs and sex drive. His years of working with asbestos and other chemicals have affected his lymph glands. His lungs are impairing the lymph glands as well and would benefit from reflexology to help increase his circulation. Leveling out his thyroid hormones can control his blood sugar level.

DIARRHEA

F 59 yrs 12-21-98

Problem: She has had life-long constipation and diarrhea.

Reading: Most of her problem is in the stomach, surrounding organs and colon. This is mostly a nerve interference problem. She needs to see a chiropractor for adjustment of a vertebra in her back just above the kidneys. She also needs Rolfing and reflexology. These practitioners need to concentrate on the stomach, gallbladder, spleen, liver, and other organs before they begin work on the colon. They should not work on the upper colon until some of the tenderness leaves this area. The Rolfing and reflexology will give her a 30% improvement. After 30 days of Rolfing and reflexology, she should then see a psychotherapist. She has energy blockage in the stomach and midsection that is emotional in origin. She wants to avoid the emotional aspect, but it cannot be avoided. She needs to drink plenty of water.

F 74 yrs 02-05-97
Problem: She has chronic diarrhea.
Reading: She has an allergic reaction to a food or vegetation in her yard, and this can be controlled or corrected readily. She needs to have an allergy test to determine what they are and avoid them accordingly.

F 18 mos 04-26-99
Problem: She has had diarrhea for 2 weeks.
Reading: The diarrhea could be caused by a parasite in the blood that is mostly disturbing the colon. She needs to be treated to rid her body of the parasites.

F 35 yrs 12-13-99
Problem: She has had diarrhea for the past 2 years that comes and goes, lasting 2 weeks at a time. She is on the blood-type diet.
Reading: She is allergic to animal hair and needs a room air purifier. Dog hair is irritating her digestive tract and causing the diarrhea. (She then stated that she has had the dog for 2 years–the same span of time that she has had the diarrhea.)

F 41 yrs 12-10-99
Problem: She was in a car accident in 1995, resulting in three spinal fusions in her neck. Her main concern today is her chronic diarrhea. X-ray film shows a shadow in the bile duct.
Reading: The diarrhea is linked to the bile duct and pancreatic area. Fiber in the bile duct likely was torn and bruised when she was in the car accident. This torn fiber has formed scar tissue, which is the shadow on the x-ray film. If this area can be treated, she will experience improvement with the diarrhea.

F 51 yrs 05-14-01
Problem: She has chronic diarrhea.

Reading: Her liver is causing her digestive problems. It is toxic and does not filter properly. Reflexology, acupuncture, and liver flushes would help.

F 74 yrs 06-23-01

Problem: She developed diarrhea 2 years ago. Doctors took her off dairy products, but it did not help. Now she is extremely bloated in her stomach and colon. Every morning she wakes up nauseated until she has a bowel movement, which she must precede with her diarrhea medication. Although digestive tests have all been negative, doctors have diagnosed her as having irritable bowel syndrome.

Reading: Her stomach appears to have shifted to one side, stretching the area that attaches her stomach to her intestines. This stretching and misalignment of the soft tissue has caused the diarrhea and bloating. (She said that many years ago when she lived in a mountain resort she used to fall a lot.) These falls likely have caused her problem, which has gone untreated for many years. Rolfing the soft tissue from the stomach to the intestines may help realign and relax the area. Acupuncture would help as well.

DIET

F 65 yrs 12-06-98

Problem: She has developed warts and moles on her midbody.

Reading: The warts and moles are blood-related. Perhaps eating according to her blood type would help.

F 32 yrs 07-03-98

Problem: She has rheumatoid arthritis.

Reading: She needs to change her diet and open up her energy. Diet is the most important factor, and stress is secondary in the arthritis flare-ups. She needs to drink purified water and take potassium. Her colon should be flushed, preferably with a laxative of some kind, but she should avoid a high-roughage bran laxative.

F 74 yrs 10-25-98
Problem: She has arthritis in the hands and hip.
Reading: She should eat according to her blood type. This will help prevent stiffness of the body and joints.

F 76 yrs 03-13-00
Problem: She has arthritis throughout the body.
Reading: She should watch her salt intake and eat according to her "O" blood-type diet. This will help her arthritis.

M 7 yrs 09-27-99
Problem: He has been angry since birth. He has to be told to do things several times and does not do what he is told. He is sensitive and cries a lot. He is prone to strep throats.
Reading: He has a lot of congestion in his forehead that is diet-related. He has chronic headaches because of the pressure. His parents need to watch his intake of processed foods, milk, cheese, sugar, and salt. He is sensitive to the processed foods, and the others are causing the congestion. If the diet does not work, he should have acupuncture and other energy work. He does not have a mental disorder. This behavior is diet-related. The strep throats will go away when his diet improves.

F 49 yrs 12-13-99
Problem: She has anemia (low RBC count) and is concerned that her high cholesterol level may affect her heart.
Reading: She is a strong candidate for eating by her blood type. Her pancreas has been affected most by her diet. She is susceptible to diabetes. The blood type diet should help prevent diabetes and anemia, and it should help control her cholesterol levels.

M 50 yrs 06-19-00
Problem: He has low back pain and stiffness in the hands, feet, and hips.
Reading: Eating by his blood type should reduce the joint discomfort.

F 54 yrs 11-24-98
Problem: She has high cholesterol.
Reading: Her cholesterol problem is partly hereditary and partly dietary. Her stress level is a factor as well. She should eat according to her blood type. Her gallbladder looks slightly toxic and has a buildup of fat. Her hearing is okay but not great, with an equal loss in both ears. Diet will help this from getting progressively worse. The high cholesterol level has not helped the hearing loss.

M 46 yrs 11-03-99
Problem: He has high cholesterol.
Reading: His diet is not compatible with his blood type, and this is causing the high cholesterol level.

F 25 yrs 04-03-00
Problem: She has migraine headaches several times a year.
Reading: Her migraine headaches are diet-related, particularly to caffeine and dairy. Red meat contributes to her weight gain.

F 61 yrs 10-01-98
Problem: Her father had Alzheimer's disease; she is concerned about getting it herself.
Reading: She might get Alzheimer's disease, but diet will control a lot of the brain loss and slow down the disease. She should eat according to her blood type.

M 40 yrs 01-24-99
Problem: He has psoriasis and believes that it is related to his stress. He also suffers from a lack of sleep. His memory is poor, and he gets

confused when he tries to make decisions. He sneezes several times throughout the day.

Reading: His psoriasis is 60% stress-related and 40% diet-related. His lack of sleep is caused by "jump starting" his pituitary gland with sugar, caffeine, and chocolate after noon. He needs to see a naturopath for an herb that will restore the pituitary gland. His lack of energy is diet-related, not an energy block. His memory loss and confusion are diet- and stress-related. Nothing is wrong with his mind. Sugar and chocolate are causing the sneezing attacks. He might also increase his intake of dietary oils. His body is becoming stiff.

M 29 yrs 04-26-99

Problem: He has sinus problems.

Reading: He has sinus pressure, mostly in the front half of his head. He has a great deal of drainage in his throat and behind his cheekbones. Dairy products contribute to this drainage. The pressure has affected his thought processes. His colon is inactive and needs roughage and more water. If he can mentally relax and eat better, he will spend less energy trying to wake up. Beer is affecting his digestion and his ability to relax. He needs to learn relaxation techniques.

F 49 yrs 03-24-00

Problem: She has a sinus problem.

Reading: Eating dairy causes her sinus problem.

M 30 yrs 07-08-00

Problem: He has had hair loss since 15 years of age. .

Reading: His diet is an important factor in his hair loss. He needs B vitamins. Also, his liver is toxic and is another link to his hair loss. He needs to avoid fried foods. Selenium would be good for his age spots and toxic liver. He should drink apple cider vinegar.

F 39 yrs 02-21-00

Problem: She has had headaches for the last 7 months and heavy menstruation for the past year.

Reading: She has a lymphatic disorder in the base of her neck near the clavicle. She needs a lymphatic treatment. She eats foods that form toxins, and the blocked lymph node prevents the toxins from moving out of the brain, causing the headaches. She needs to eat according to her blood type. This will diminish the toxins and improve the headaches within 3 months. Her heavy menstruation is linked to her hormone level, which is a reaction to her diet. She may need hormone supplements if she changes her diet.

M 55 yrs 01-28-98

Problem: He has had recent chest discomfort and is concerned about his heart.

Reading: His heart is okay. The problem lies behind the heart or chest area. He has digestive problems, heartburn, and obesity. He has a lining of fat around his heart, but it has not yet affected the heart. He needs to cut back on caffeine. The caffeine is stimulating his heart and contributing to a narrowing of the arteries, which is speeding up his heartbeat. The acid in both citrus and caffeine beverages is contributing to the heartburn.

F 39 yrs 11-01-98

Problem: She is 65 pounds overweight. Her neck and lower back do not hold alignment, she has joint pain, and her digestive system and kidneys are a concern. She has frequent yeast infections, and she thinks they are sugar-related.

Reading: She craves salt and eats a lot of foods with sodium used as a preservative. She needs to eat more natural foods and avoid salt completely. It causes her to retain water weight and is bothering her digestive system. She has a problem with her sweat glands, which are slow to react and cause her to hold salt. She also does not eat regular meals. Sometimes she eats twice a day and sometimes four times a day. She needs to plan meals and eat before she gets too hungry. She will have less joint pain when she reduces her salt intake.

F 59 yrs 01-25-99
Problem: She has joint and general body stiffness. She is having trouble losing weight.
Reading: Her weight bothers her, but she has not had a reason to lose it until now (her age). She needs to focus on her blood-type diet and avoid breads especially. She is strong willed and can accomplish great things if she wants to. She needs to breathe properly and stretch. She is stiff because of a lack of exercise and poor diet.

M 39 yrs 09-13-99
Problem: He has painful knees. His liver enzymes are high, and his doctors are concerned.
Reading: The liver problem is diet-related. He needs to eat according to his blood type and get off salt. He retains water, which is causing knee pain. He needs to take herbs to treat the liver.

F 56 yrs 11-18-99
Problem: She has long-term sinus congestion and is overweight.
Reading: The sinus congestion is mostly diet-related. Eating according to her blood type would help her sinuses and weight problem.

F 45 yrs 01-31-99
Problem: She has tenderness in her breasts.
Reading: She should eat according to her blood type. She is sensitive to caffeine, and her breasts become tender when she uses it.

F 27 yrs 05-08-00
Problem: She has irregular periods, but the flow is normal. She also has a skin rash that resembles hives and has been warm and itchy for 3 years.
Reading: Both her liver and pancreas are toxic and are linked to the irregular periods and the rash. Fried foods are the cause. She needs to flush both organs with herbs.

M 34 yrs 06-18-98
Problem: He is concerned about his weight.
Reading: While his alcohol consumption is an emotional issue, his food consumption is not—he just enjoys it. He should eat according to his blood type. Emotionally he is ready to handle the weight loss now because he would be doing it for himself, not for others.

F 39 yrs 10-04-99
Problem: She has a low sex drive and is overweight.
Reading: Salt is influencing her weight because she is retaining water. Her low sex drive is mostly physical—she is too heavy. Salt is also affecting this drive. She needs more protein, fewer carbohydrates, and more exercise. She also needs to drink more water.

F 54 yrs 05-29-00
Problem: She has gained 100 pounds.
Reading: She needs to cut out salt. Learning to breathe properly would help her with her chocolate cravings.

F 29 yrs 02-12-00
Problem: She has had scoliosis since childhood.
Reading: Her diet is a factor. She is very sensitive to food and needs to eat according to her blood type, consuming the highly beneficial foods only.

F 55 yrs 01-07-00
Problem: She has headaches, back pain, hip pain, and pain in the bottoms of her feet, which she believes was brought on by car accidents.
Reading: She is low in minerals, especially potassium. She also needs enzymes for the digestive tract. Half of her body pain is physical, and the other half is emotional. Something is keeping her from wanting to get completely better. Eating according to her blood type would be beneficial and help eliminate some of the toxins in her blood, which in turn would reduce the back and hip pain.

F 70 yrs 02-04-01
Problem: She has asthma. She also has bloating and a lot of stomach acid.
Reading: She is not handling the high fiber and vegetable content of her diet, so she is probably an "O" blood type. (She agreed that she is and stated that she feels better when she follows the blood-type diet and not as well when her diet is high in fiber.) Her asthma is a reaction to the grains that she eats.

F 45 yrs 12-10-00
Problem: She has circulatory problems and leg and vein discomfort.
Reading: High cholesterol is the issue with her circulation, leg, and vein problems. Eating according to her blood type would help her.

F 43 yrs 03-04-01
Problem: She has had breast cancer in the right breast twice in the past 13 years. She now has a breast implant. Lately she has been experiencing pain under the left ribs with cold then searing hot pain. Doctors believe it is a hiatal hernia with esophageal inflammation. She is taking acid suppression medication for it and the pain has improved by 50%, but she still has bloating and cannot sleep well at night.
Reading: The breast cancer was caused by toxic blood, which in turn was caused by her spleen. In addition, her hormones have been imbalanced for 10 years, and this combination is behind the recurring breast cancer. The spleen is the cause of her bloating as well as her pain. She needs to have an x-ray examination of the spleen.

The most important thing she can do for her health and to avoid another cancer is to eat according to her blood type. The foods that she eats are incompatible with her blood type and the cause of her toxic blood. She should also have energy work through her reproductive system. After all of this is done, she should have her hormone levels checked.

M 46 yrs 11-03-99
Problem: He has itching hemorrhoids.

Reading: His diet is not compatible with his blood type and is contributing to his hemorrhoids.

M 40 yrs 01-24-99
Problem: He sneezes several times throughout the day.
Reading: Sugar and chocolate are causing the sneezing attacks.

DIGESTIVE PROBLEMS

F 38 yrs 11-26-99
Problem: She has a sensation of not being able to move food beyond the esophagus and digest it properly.
Reading: Her esophagus is fine. Too much salt intake and not enough water cause her symptoms.

F 69 yrs 12-21-98
Problem: Her digestive area has energy blockage.
Reading: She is a self-healing person. She needs to get out and go dancing and meet men. This will open up her emotional side, which will help open up her energy in the digestive system. Her overall physical health is very good.

F 60 yrs 03-03-98
Problem: She is concerned about digestion and elimination.
Reading: The colon has a lot of gas, probably caused by the gallbladder. She should have her gallbladder flushed, which would have good results. Reflexology also would help the gallbladder. Elimination will be easier once she gets the colon under control. Both the small intestine and colon have trouble transferring the food products, which results in

constipation. Flushing the colon would be helpful, but she should be careful that the product does not further irritate the colon. A mild laxative rather than a product that is high in roughage would be best.

F 49 yrs 10-17-96
Problem: She has had diarrhea and constipation for 18 months and pain in her digestive system and colon area. She has had several colonic enemas.

Reading: Most likely her stomach is having a toxic reaction to pesticide spray, dish soap, and laundry detergents. She also could be reacting to air pollution. She should avoid chemicals and pools and spas because of the chlorine. She has a blockage in the upper portion of her colon. This problem is most likely related to toxins, as are the constipation and abdominal pain. The liver is slightly toxic as well. The toxic buildup may get worse if she does not get it under control. She should stop the colonics. They may be slightly irritating to the stomach and are not helping anyway. She might try saunas to sweat out the toxins in her body. She should be sure that her clothes, bedclothes, and dishes are rinsed well; drink purified water; and breathe clean air. After making these changes, she will respond positively.

M 59 yrs 07-01-97
Problem: He has pain in the upper stomach that occurs in the middle of the night, waking him up. The pain is so bad that he cannot get back to sleep. Several diagnostic tests have been negative.

Reading: His parotid glands are not producing enough saliva, and his blood supply to the stomach is either inadequate or lacks oxygen. These problems are causing the stomach to spasm or cramp while he is sleeping.

M 14 yrs 02-08-98
Problem: He was diagnosed at 5 years of age with a condition causing internal hemorrhaging of the colon. It can affect the kidneys and other organs when he gets older.

Reading: His colon is enlarged and continually irritated; therefore it is sensitive to pesticides and environmental pollution. Although he needs to avoid carbonated and citrus drinks, he will become ill much quicker with what he breathes than with what he eats. His parents should avoid spraying pesticides inside the home and adding chlorine in concentrated amounts to the water.

He will suffer from stomach problems when he is an adult. Of all the chemicals, pesticides would be the worst. His lungs are very sensitive to chemical agents and could easily be affected. This needs to be closely monitored because he already has inflammation in the lower lungs. He should bathe with a natural, nonchemical soap.

F 70 yrs 10-13-98

Problem: She has poor digestion.

Reading: The upper digestive area is not in good condition. The problem appears to be a parasite in the lining of the colon. For this reason the vitamins and minerals in her food are not processing through her body.

F 46 yrs 11-23-98

Problem: She has difficulty with digestion.

Reading: Her problems with digestion are partly allergy-related from a food group and partly from airborne pollens or grass. She needs to rinse her foods or boil them before eating them because of the pesticides. Although sugar is affecting her sinuses more than her digestive tract, sugar does upset her stomach because her digestive tract cannot handle it. Her digestive problem is also nerve-related, coming from the mid-back just below the shoulders. She needs reflexology to stimulate this area and maybe a chiropractic adjustment.

F 37 yrs 12-01-98

Problem: She believes that her digestive system is sensitive to food. She says that she feels better since taking vitamins and minerals. She states that her cecum (first part of the large intestine that connects to the ileum of the small intestine) feels as though it has trapped energy.

Reading: Her stomach has a high level of acid, and the areas that connect the stomach to the esophagus and small intestine are irritated. This is also emotionally related. She has a fear of eating because she thinks the food will cause discomfort when she digests it. She needs a medication that will relax the stomach area, break down the gases, and soothe the irritation before eating. The vitamins and minerals have been beneficial, but not for her digestive system. Eating more proteins has been more effective in controlling her sugar cravings than the vitamins and minerals have. Her cecum does have energy blockage, and it needs energy work and more dietary oils. She should also reduce slightly her intake of vitamins and minerals.

F 59 yrs 01-11-99

Problem: She had colon surgery 2 years ago.

Reading: She never fully recovered from colon surgery physically or emotionally. Her body needs to be retrained in eating and digesting. She should eat smaller portions more frequently throughout the day. Eating according to her blood type would help, and she should drink a glass of water with each meal.

F 54 yrs 03-15-99

Problem: She has a history of digestive disorders, including gas and bloating in the colon. She has been diagnosed with celiac disease (gluten intolerance). Upper and lower gastrointestinal tests were negative, as was the MRI for her pancreas.

Reading: She needs energy work in the colon, upper stomach, liver, and gallbladder up through the center of her chest. She needs herbal enzymes because the enzymes in her colon are depleted as a result of radiation exposure. She also needs to detoxify from the radiation.

F 44 yrs 03-29-99

Problem: She has had a bowel disorder for 20 years. If she does not take an enema every day, she cannot have a bowel movement.

Reading: She has an emotional energy blockage that stems from an event in the early 1970s. This blockage runs at a 45-degree angle through her body from the upper side of her head, down through the chest and colon (missing the stomach), and ending above the knees. It has a very wide path. She needs to eat according to her blood type, work on her emotional state, see a hypnotherapist, and have energy work. This combination will help her.

F 55 yrs 04-20-99

Problem: She has poor digestion and chronic constipation for which she has tried herbs, but they have not helped. She believes that she is intolerant of dairy products.

Reading: The constipation may be linked to allergies or chemicals. She has a lot of energy blockage to her front half, starting at the pubic area and traveling upward to the neck. The entire digestive area is blocked, which is why she has difficulty digesting and constipation. She is not intolerant of dairy products–she just cannot digest them because of the energy blockage. She needs energy work, reflexology, acupuncture, relaxation (e.g., yoga), and plenty of liquids.

F 3 yrs 12-02-99

Problem: She has had digestive problems since birth and was diagnosed with malabsorption (inability to absorb nutrients). She has trouble gaining weight and is now on a hypoallergenic diet.

Reading: The pancreas appears to be the main problem area, affecting her liver and perhaps her gallbladder and colon. She needs digestive enzymes and more vitamins and minerals. Acupuncture or reflexology should be used to stimulate the pancreas. The strict diet is not a cure, although it is keeping her from becoming worse. However, it appears to be robbing her of some nutrients. Supplements would help.

M 33 yrs 12-09-99

Problem: He is not absorbing his foods well and cannot gain weight. He has pain or burning in his digestive tract, both knees bother him, and he had valley fever 5 years ago. He is concerned that the mercury fillings in his teeth are causing some of his problems.

Reading: His digestive enzymes are low, and he does not have enough good bacteria in his colon. The digestive problem is more physical than stress-related. The valley fever is most likely the cause of the depletion of his good bacteria. He is low in vitamins and minerals because of the poor dietary absorption, and this has contributed to some of his knee pain. He needs to drink more water and increase the good bacteria in his colon. The mercury fillings are not a current issue, but they may be in the next 4 years.

F 7 yrs 03-07-00

Reading: She has chronic stomach pain and constipation. She has been on herbs for a month with little results. An abdominal x-ray examination was negative.

Reading: Her heart is not sending normal amounts of blood to the digestive area, which in turn is causing the digestive disorder and constipation. She probably tires quickly or easily and perhaps experiences shortness of breath from time to time. She also appears to be experiencing muscle aches in the thighs as a result of the lack of circulation. Her mother confirmed that her daughter had a heart murmur at 2 years of age. She needs medical follow-up for this problem.

F 76 yrs 03-13-00

Problem: She has stomach upset, vomiting, and diarrhea.

Reading: The vomiting and foul tastes in her mouth occur because of the high acid content in her stomach. To improve her digestive condition she needs to watch her salt intake and eat by an "O" blood-type diet.

F 53 yrs 03-23-00

Problem: She has had a strange feeling in her intestine for 2 months. She was treated for ulcers and had several tests, but the tests are negative and ulcer treatment has not helped.

Reading: Gases are trapped in the colon. She needs a liquid diet for 1 to 3 days. This will clear up the colon and decrease the gases. She also needs to eat according to her blood type and avoid caffeine. Acupuncture will open up energy to the digestive organs.

M 29 yrs 05-08-00

Problem: He has blood in the stool, acid reflux, ulcers, vomiting, and bowel movements 4 to 6 times every morning.

Reading: He has a hard time gaining weight and likely has a parasite. He needs to flush his liver and avoid alcohol. He eats foods with too much grease; he should avoid fried foods.

F 46 yrs 06-29-99

Problem: She has a lazy or slow digestive system, constipation, and gas. Her energy level drops off around 4 PM every day.

Reading: She has an energy blockage in her digestive tract. She needs energy work from the lower esophagus to the stomach, down through the duodenum, and into the upper colon. After 3 weeks of energy work and herbs for flushing the area, she should then undergo colonic enema treatments. She could also stay on the energy and herb program, and in 60 days she will feel much better. Currently her body rejects sugar, but this will no longer occur once her digestion problem is fixed.

F 27 yrs 04-05-99

Problem: She was diagnosed with lupus. Her naturopathic doctor believes that she has too much mercury in her teeth. She has been diagnosed with leaky gut syndrome as well.

Reading: She likely does not have lupus. The naturopathic doctor is right about the high mercury level in her blood stream, but she is also high in other minerals such as copper and aluminum. Her liver is toxic, and her pancreas is exhausted. The leaky gut will not get completely better until these organs have been restored. She needs help, such as hypnosis, in dealing with stress. The brain is releasing (or overproducing) minerals, most likely as a result of the pituitary gland being stressed and in need of restoration. She needs reflexology to treat the pituitary gland, pancreas, and liver.

F 32 yrs 03-29-99

Problem: She has joint pain, mainly in the knees. The bottoms of her feet and her hands are affected as well. A rheumatologist has not found anything wrong with her joints. A podiatrist prescribed corrective shoes for flat feet, but they have not helped either.

Reading: Her blood is toxic, stemming from her liver and stomach and possibly her gallbladder. Her stomach is the main problem. It has a high content of fatty buildup, and the liver is tired from working on the problem. This has affected her blood, which in turn has affected her joints. She does not produce enough enzymes to dissolve her food. First she needs to see a naturopath for an herb that will cleanse the stomach and liver. Then she needs a product that will help her dissolve her foods. She could start with apple cider vinegar.

F 72 yrs 08-02-97

Problem: She has gastric irritation. Gastrointestinal tests were negative.

Reading: Her problem in the upper diaphragmatic area could be liver-related. Her liver is toxic. This could be a nerve problem caused by a vertebra in her back. She should see a naturopathic doctor for cleansing the liver and a chiropractor for the problem with the vertebra.

M 2 1/2 yrs 03-15-99

Problem: He was diagnosed with colic at birth and still wakes up at night complaining that his stomach hurts. He has diarrhea four to five times a day. When surrounded by other people he gets hyperactive, cannot speak, hits his head on the wall, and bites others. Medical tests are normal, and doctors believe that he should see a psychologist, although they have considered wheat or dairy intolerance as the cause.

Reading: Part of his problem is psychological and stems from when he was in his mother's womb. He becomes confused when he is around a lot of people and gets scared. His brain looks enlarged or overly developed for his age, and he should be seen by a neurologist. His back from the waist up is red and hot, and his chest is cold. He needs energy work to the front half of his body, with his brain as the main focus.

F 70 yrs 02-04-01

Problem: She believes that her transverse colon has prolapsed and her stomach has fallen in this area. She also has bloating and a lot of stomach acid.

Reading: Most likely the splenic vein is the main reason for her digestive problems. Thirty minutes of reflexology to the spleen would be good. She also reacts to the high fiber and vegetable content of her diet and is probably an "O" blood type. (She confirmed that she is an "O" blood type and said that she feels better when she is on the diet and less well when she eats foods that are high in fiber.)

M 49 yrs 01-22-01

Problem: He has been treated with acupuncture for the past 4 years for body tenderness, fatigue, and a stomach disorder. He has seen small improvements, but now surgeons want to repair a valve in his stomach. Stomach acid backs up into his throat and airway.

Reading: He has an energy blockage that runs from the top of his head into his chest. This was caused by an emotional issue that was very serious and occurred when he was a young adult in his early twenties. (He then explained that when he was in his twenties his mother had been struck and killed by a car.) He has not sufficiently dealt with this death emotionally, and it has manifested in his body. He needs a slow approach to acupuncture and energy work, starting first with the energy work. Treatment should start at the top of his head and gradually work down so that he can handle the treatments. Hypnotherapy should unlock some of the illness if treatments are successful. He might delay his gastric surgery for about a month to see if hypnotherapy and energy work help improve his digestive disorder.

F 43 yrs 09-20-00

Problem: She has irritable bowel syndrome. Medication is not helping her.

Reading: She lacks digestive enzymes. She should see a naturopath for digestive enzymes.

F 51 yrs 01-28-01

Problem: She has had chronic vomiting for 5 years and recently has been vomiting blood. She has had pain near her spleen for the last 5 years as well. This past year the hair in the back of her head started falling out. She is very tired and cannot keep her eyes open. Her mother died of bone cancer, and she is concerned because her bones have begun aching.

Reading: Her pituitary gland is irregular and dripping hormones slowly like a faucet that cannot be turned off. The aching in her bones is hormone-related as well. The lower heart valves cause the pain near the spleen. They are not blocked; they just are not performing properly because of the hormones. Getting more oxygen into the blood would help her heart. Apple cider vinegar might help the heart valves, as well as long walks and lying on a recline board (head lower than the feet). The area between her eyes is affected as well. Emotions have caused these problems. She has a tendency to think negatively, and she needs a spiritual reunion with God.

M 55 yrs 05-05-01

Problem: He has had chronic nausea for the past 2 years, which is causing him much anxiety. He also has chest pain and burning, but ECGs and other tests have been negative. Recently he has increased his water intake, which seems to help him.

Reading: He has an electrical imbalance in his brain that crisscrosses over his forehead, eyes, center of his brain, and thyroid gland. Hormones are low from the thyroid gland as a result, affecting his sex drive and muscle tone mainly in the upper portion of his body. His stomach appears quiet and lacking digestive processes because of this energy imbalance. Digestive enzymes are absent as a result, which creates the difficulty with digestion and nausea. Water helps his digestion, but without the digestive enzymes he will continue to have the problem. He needs to raise the level of hormones from the thyroid gland and take digestive enzymes and minerals that contribute to digestion. Most importantly, he needs energy work to the brain to open this area back up and reverse the crisscross to the center of his brain. This is where the disruption has occurred, throwing off the normal balance of nutritional chemicals from the brain and preventing them from reaching the colon.

M 70 yrs 08-19-01
Problem: He has had digestive problems all of his life, including heartburn, indigestion, burning, stomach ulcers, and a bacterial infection that affects the stomach lining.
Reading: A vertebra in his occipital area is out of place. This has disturbed the alignment of his esophagus and, in turn, has affected his digestive enzymes. One reason for the bacterial infection is his lack of digestive fluids that normally would manage and control the bacteria in his stomach. He should see a chiropractor to realign his neck and esophagus and a Rolfer or acupuncturist to treat and adjust the esophagus and thus ensure the normal flow and proportion of digestive fluids into his stomach.

DIZZINESS

M 46 yrs 01-25-99
Problem: He has had dizziness and ringing in the right ear for 3 years. A large drum fell on him in an industrial accident, and he was told that he would never leave a wheelchair.
Reading: Tight ligaments in his neck cause the dizziness and ringing in his ear. Stress is pulling his head and neck down into his shoulders, restricting the nerves in his ear and affecting the ear canal. A Rolfer should work on the back of his neck, down into the trapezius muscles and clavicle area. Once this area is freed up, the stress will not affect this area as much and he should not experience the ringing or dizziness.

F 73 yrs 08-02-97
Problem: Doctors say that her heart is the cause of her dizziness or fainting spells. A pacemaker was implanted to control her dizziness.
Reading: Her heart is not the problem. It may be the front portion of her brain. She may have Alzheimer's disease.

F 78 yrs 03-08-99
Problem: She has dizzy spells that to her feel like a lack of circulation. An MRI was negative. She also has numbness in her hands and feet.
Reading: She does not have nerve or circulation problems. She is low in minerals, particularly potassium and sodium, which is why she is dizzy. She should see a naturopath for minerals.

F 65 yrs 03-03-01
Problem: She has had dizziness, headaches, and chills for 2 years. Three chiropractors have been unable to tell her the cause. She fell backward during one episode 5 months ago and pulled muscles in the back of her leg.
Reading: Hormones from her adrenal gland are low, and she gets dizzy when she moves quickly or becomes tired. This is also the reason for her headaches and chills. The adrenal gland should be treated with acupuncture and herbs. After about 60 days of this treatment, her hormone levels should be checked; if they are low, she should begin an adrenal hormone.

M 53 yrs 03-12-01
Problem: He has been experiencing dizziness and pressure in his head for the past year. Although these symptoms are less severe at night, they affect him greatly during the day. He has had many diagnostic tests that have all been negative.
Reading: One side of his sinus has an obstruction, possibly a tumor. Everything else looks fine. He needs to have his sinuses checked.

DRUGS/MEDICATIONS, REACTIONS TO

M 42 yrs 02-12-01

Problem: He was diagnosed with chronic fatigue. Doctors have been unable to determine the cause or cure. He has been taking vitamin B_{12} injections and antiseizure medications to help him sleep. He wakes up very tired with muscle and joint pain.

Reading: The first vertebra in his neck is locked down, driving pain straight down his spine. His head appears to be tilted back, his chin is up, his jaw joint is very tight, and he has pressure on his brain. (He agreed that he gets headaches in the back of his head and off to the left side.) Vitamin B_{12} injections and antiseizure medication will not help him. First he needs Rolfing to the neck and then the back of the head, followed by the jaw joint. Then he needs acupuncture to open the energy to the jaw, cheeks, and bottom teeth. The swelling in the brain looks medicine-related. (He then stated that as a child he overdosed on aspirin.)

F 54 yrs 02-14-01

Problem: She was diagnosed with multiple sclerosis based on clinical symptoms. Within 3 years of this diagnosis she was no longer able to walk.

Reading: She has a dark and hollow look to the front brain and sinus area. It appears that she was exposed to a drug 20 years ago. (She then concurred that when she was in her early twenties she used LSD approximately 20 times.) She would benefit from acupuncture to the area of the brain that affects mood, speech, and motor function.

F 49 yrs 04-30-01

Problem: She lost all but the peripheral vision in her right eye 1 year ago when a blood vessel ruptured. All tests have been negative, and she wants to know what caused this.

Reading: Her blood was exposed to something, probably a medication. This toxic blood pumped into the blood vessels in the brain. (She stated that she works in a photo lab with poor ventilation.) This may be part of the problem, but a drug was the likely trigger. (She then recalled that cortisone was injected into her wrist a year ago.)

EAR/HEARING PROBLEMS

F 12 yrs 02-08-98

Problem: Her parents requested a reading for her.

Reading: She could suffer from ear infections because of a buildup of wax and fluid. She needs a chiropractor to adjust her upper neck to free up the ears. Her neck should be adjusted routinely to avoid ear infections.

M 44 yrs 06-29-99

Problem: He has had a chronic whistle in the right ear for the last 3 years. He lost his balance and could not get out of bed 6 months ago.

Reading: His sinus passages are narrow, even up through the forehead. He could use energy work to the back of his head and neck. His ear rings less when it is dry than when it is wet. The ringing is structural, not nerve-related, and may be fixed through surgery.

F 57 yrs 02-01-99

Problem: She has a sensation of motion or earthquake; she cannot keep her balance or walk a straight line. When she lies down she feels as though she is on a waterbed. Doctors cannot find anything wrong; an MRI was negative. This problem began when she stopped taking her medication for depression.

Reading: The motion in her head is related to her ears. She has extremely good hearing. Her ear canals are wider than normal, which has caused her sensitivity to sounds and vibrations. This is not the cause of her motion problem, but it is the reason that she feels the motion. She needs to muffle the hearing and then work on the cause.

F 61 yrs 10-01-98

Problem: She has distortion in the left ear and does not hear well.

Reading: The ear problem is more emotional than physical. She has selective hearing, which is her way of blocking out stress.

F 54 yrs 11-24-98

Problem: She has high cholesterol.

Reading: Her cholesterol problem is partly hereditary and partly dietary. Her stress level is a factor. Her hearing is okay but not great, and she has an equal loss in both ears. Diet will help this from getting progressively worse, and the high cholesterol level has not helped the problem.

M 46 yrs 01-25-99

Problem: He has had ringing in his right ear for 3 years. A large drum fell on him in an industrial accident, and he was told that he would never leave a wheelchair.

Reading: Tight neck ligaments are causing the ringing in his ear. Stress is pulling his head and neck down into his shoulders, restricting the nerves in his ear and affecting the ear canal. A Rolfer should work on the back of the neck, down into the trapezius muscles and clavicle area. Once this area is freed up, the stress will not affect this area as much and he will not experience the ringing.

M 42 yrs 02-13-97

Problem: He has had ringing in the ears for the past 5 years. One ear is worse than the other and rings constantly.

Reading: He needs to avoid pressurized places, which was the likely cause (probably airplane pressure). Although the problem was not originally stress-related, stress causes a rush of blood to the base of his skull upward through the back of his head, resulting in a disruption to the ears and an intensification of the ringing. When these blood vessels are not as pressurized, the ringing subsides. He should use cold packs to the back of his head and play soft music via a headset. This may help him relax by *not* concentrating on the ringing, therefore reducing the swelling to the vessels and hence the ringing in the ears. Soft music would be better than no music at all. He needs to tilt his head back when he uses the cold pack. This will reduce the swelling to the blood vessels and help prevent them from pulsating. At times he attempts to think or concentrate on more than one thing at a time. He should avoid this because it increases the ringing.

M 52 yrs 04-14-98

Problem: He has lost 85% of his hearing.

Reading: Weight gain, sugar ingestion, allergy and sinus problems, and past smoking have caused a narrowing in the upper portion of his throat. This has brought on the early hearing loss. He needs to cut down on sugar, fats, and dairy. Although the hearing will not get better, he might be able to prevent it from getting worse.

F 62 yrs 04-23-98

Problem: She has a sensation of pressure and can hear sounds in one ear. She caught a virus 3 months earlier that caused the bridge of her nose to swell, and she then began to have a buildup of fluids in the ear.

Reading: Mucus built up in her ear as a result of the virus, and this led to pressure on a nerve, which is causing the sounds. These sounds will likely go away. The nerve can restore to about 80% to 90% through reflexology. It may completely restore, but more likely it will not.

M 40 yrs 01-24-99

Problem: He has had ringing in the ears for the last 2 years.

Reading: The ringing in his ears is stress-related. He needs to see a therapist who specializes in stress-related issues.

F 52 yrs 06-02-01

Problem: She has had ringing in the ears for the past 3 years. She also has high cholesterol and is under a lot of family stress.

Reading: The ringing in her ears is caused by pressure in a vein that runs along the side of her neck. Her lymphatic system is getting clogged and needs to be drained. She should have lymphatic massage or reflexology to the lymphatic system in the chest and armpits to promote drainage. She also needs to reduce her cholesterol so that the neck vein does not get worse. Her adrenal glands are 50% depleted as a result of stress and are raising her cholesterol level.

F 74 yrs 06-10-01

Problem: She has spells of extreme fatigue and weakness while exerting or walking and can barely get back home. She has a lot of stress in her marriage and wonders if her emotions could be causing this problem. Medical tests have all come back normal, and doctors have been unable to diagnose her condition.

Reading: She has an inner ear problem and should see an ear specialist. (She then stated that she has extremely sensitive ears and noises bother her. She can even hear neighbors talking when she is inside her home.) A nerve in her ear becomes stimulated by noise. It in turn transfers this stimulation to the portion of the brain that controls motor functions, and she becomes instantly weak.

ELECTRONIC/VOLTAGE PROBLEMS

M 54 yrs 01-27-01

Problem: He has had light-headedness with loss of balance for 6 months. His neurologist believes that he may have diabetes. He now suffers from headaches and numbness in the right side of his head, and he is very tired.

Reading: He has a "V" shaped, deep energy blockage on the top of his head that appears to have a nerve-brain connection. This is a disruption caused by electrical airwaves, perhaps from mobile phones, antennas, or high-power voltage. If exposure is eliminated, he has an 80% chance of total recovery. If he does not eliminate the exposure, he will continue to get worse. He needs energy opened from the navel up and out through the digestive system, lungs, chest, and shoulders. This will prevent any future disorder. He needs acupuncture to the brain for the nerve disorder and acupuncture to the body for energy. (He then explained that he works at the airport, where there are many electronic waves.)

M 49 yrs 02-17-01

Problem: He has had many different rare diseases diagnosed in the last 10 years, including diabetes insipidus, a bone disease, back degeneration, and a brain disorder. He takes morphine and codeine daily for pain. He wants to know how this happened. He had head trauma 17 years ago and questions if that was the cause.

Reading: From one temple to the other he appears to have abnormal wetness caused by electrical interference. His thyroid is hyperactive as a reaction to this exposure. (He said that he had been electrocuted 20 years earlier.) This electricity traveled first through the brain, then down through the thyroid, crossing in an X-fashion through the chest and out through the male organs and thighs. He looks as though he is standing in place shocked and cannot stop trembling because of the electricity. He has been left with a nerve disorder that looks as though it could be reversed with electrical stimulation to the center of the brain. In other words, shocking him again likely would stop the trembling.

M 41 yrs 03-28-01

Problem: He has chronic facial acne for which he has tried many remedies to little effect. He also has red eyelids, which do not itch or burn but increase in redness as the day goes on. He also has a light brown coating to his tongue that he can brush off, but it returns again within a few hours. Two years ago he began having a vibration sensation in his entire body except for his head and neck. This occurs when he is at rest or beginning to fall asleep. A neurologist has not been able to find a cause.

Reading: The cause appears to be an irregular neuron disorder in his brain in the area that controls sensory and visual processes. This is the basis for the vibration sensation and is affecting the spleen and thyroid, which are the cause of the acne, tongue, and eyelid problems and blood issues. The neuron disorder appears to have been triggered by an electrical shock exposure of some kind between 9 and 12 years of age. (He then said that he shocked himself on his mother's electric blender at 10 years of age.)

F 59 yrs 04-23-01

Problem: She has been very constipated and has had a foul odor to her urine for the past 4 years. Doctors put her on antibiotics, and the odor returns when she discontinues them. She began having ear and neck pain, chills, and sweats 3 years ago. She has been on medication for the pain for the past 3 years. Exploratory surgery for brain cancer was negative, although an MRI revealed three nodules on her thyroid. She was also diagnosed with chronic fatigue and a 50% blockage of her coronary arteries, and she has been told that her spleen is the cause of her abdominal pain. Occasionally the veins in her left hand and arm feel hot and swell, and the skin on her hand breaks out and turns blue. She has been to 27 different types of doctors in the past 4 years.

Reading: A natural body chemical in her brain, perhaps one that releases in response to pain, is no longer being released or produced. The absence of this chemical is causing the odor and neck, head, and ear pain. This chemical stopped being produced as a result of a high-frequency exposure or vibration, perhaps from cordless phones or computers. (She then stated that she suspects that it is cellular phones because her problems began just after she started using them.) This natural brain chemical needs to be identified so that she can be treated. She will see a great improvement once she has been treated.

F 78 yrs 05-09-01

Problem: She has been sensitive to radio frequency waves for the past 20 years. Doctors have told her to move away from power lines, transmitters, magnetic tools, and even compact discs. She moved 10 years ago and feels better, but she still has problems. She is sensitive to fats, oils, rich foods, perfumes, and chemicals, and she becomes nauseated when she is exposed to them. The problem starts with the cells in her body, then she becomes nauseated, and then her muscles may vibrate. This can last for up to 3 days. Any kind of electrical appliance can set her off as well as wind or having a wet face.

Reading: At one time she became very wet and cold, which caused her to be sick with chills and fever. This disrupted her energy flow, blocking it from traveling upward, and the energy stirs around in her abdomen. She should have acupuncture to three areas of her body–the ankles, reproductive area, and kidneys–to restore energy flow throughout her entire body.

F 56 yrs 06-23-01

Problem: For the past 8 years she has had the ability to turn lights out as she walks or drives past them, including an entire row of streetlights or lights in a supermarket. She also drains the batteries in her cell phones very quickly. This does not occur all the time, but she believes it happens most often when she is under a lot of stress.

Reading: Her brain is divided or separated more than normal. The gap between the right brain and left brain is unusually great. She is able to think or see almost like a horse or any animal whose eyes are set to the side of the head. She is close to being able to think of two things at the same time because of the unusual brain separation. This has interfered with the flow of energy through the top of her head and is why she has a high tolerance to pain—the endorphins or chemicals in her brain are divided, which has raised her pain threshold. Acupuncture would narrow or close the energy field in her brain. This would decrease the energy field, reduce the problems she is having with lights, and help control the chemicals in her brain. Acupuncture also would help restore the pituitary and hypothalamus glands because the brain separation has caused a chemical imbalance.

ENDOMETRIOSIS

F 42 yrs 12-11-98

Problem: She was diagnosed with endometriosis 3 years ago. She also has facial acne.

Reading: The worst part is over regarding the endometriosis. If it continues to cause problems, it will spread to the backside toward the spine and kidneys, not upward or forward. Exercise, diet, and supplements are all important in controlling the problem, although they will not prevent it from spreading. The supplements are the most effective, and she has room for improvement in this area. Once she goes through menopause, the condition will improve greatly. At times she feels heavy in the lower digestive or stomach area. This is yeast-and starch-related.

Eliminating these types of food can improve the acne and slightly improve the endometriosis.

F 26 yrs 02-19-01
Problem: She has endometriosis with large clots on the uterus and right ovary. She is taking injections to prevent her menstrual periods. She wants to know what is causing it and the best treatment. She also has knee displacement.
Reading: Her knee displacement is related to her hips, which are displaced as well, throwing her lumbar area and upper torso forward. The lumbar area is weak, and surprisingly this weakness is stirring the blocked energy in the center of her brain, causing confusion, impaired decision-making, and nervousness. The stressed nerves in her lower back also cause the endometriosis. She needs adjustment and treatments to her lower back, followed by acupuncture and reflexology for her brain. After that she needs Rolfing for her pelvic area, followed by chiropractic treatments to that area.

EYE/VISION PROBLEMS

F 74 yrs 10-25-98
Problem: Her right eye has had two hemorrhages; she also experiences "flashing" in that eye.
Reading: Her eye has been affected by stress. A vein in the front part of the brain at the center of the forehead pulsates with the pressure of the blood that is increased with stress. It travels down at a 45-degree angle across the center of the forehead and behind the right eye, resulting in hemorrhage and flashing. She might use a cold pack on her forehead and eye.

F 52 yrs 06-29-99
Problem: She has blurry eyesight.
Reading: Very low levels of minerals and some vitamins cause the blurry eyesight.

F 66 yrs 10-05-99
Problem: She has had itchy eyes for the past 2 years. Sometimes the blood vessels in her eyes bleed.
Reading: Her eyes are sensitive to light, which is why they tear. She should wear sunglasses and use eye drops for dryness. Airborne pollens also irritate her eyes. The bleeding blood vessel problem is mainly the result of sun exposure.

F 25 yrs 06-14-99
Problem: Her eyes became unequally dilated 6 months ago.
Reading: She has no tumors or blood disorders. Her eye condition is caused by her emotions. She is scared about life and what the future holds. She is not close to her mother, which has caused life-long emotional stress. Physical symptoms of stress began early in her childhood, but she did not identify with them. She is very sensitive and can pick up easily on the emotions of others. She needs to share her emotions more freely and see a hypnotherapist who would take her back to her childhood and work on the emotions through the years.

F 65 yrs 12-06-98
Problem: Her eyes are blood-shot.
Reading: The blood-shot eyes could be related to food sensitivity.

F 49 yrs 04-30-01
Problem: She lost all but the peripheral vision in her right eye 1 year ago when a blood vessel ruptured. All tests have been negative, and she wants to know what caused this.
Reading: Her blood was exposed to something, probably a medication, and was pumped into the blood vessels in the brain. (She stated that she

works in a photo lab with poor ventilation.) This may be part of the problem, but a drug was the likely trigger. (She then recalled that cortisone was injected into her wrist a year ago.)

F 78 yrs 04-14-01

Problem: She was diagnosed with macular degeneration 2 years ago.

Reading: The upper portions of her eyes are better than the lower portions; therefore the disease will develop slowly. She has at least 5 years of sight left and perhaps will have some sight for the rest of her life. Stimulating the nerves to her eyes will help slow the disease. Reflexology would be good for this. Sunlight exposure and possibly acupuncture would help as well.

F 61 yrs 04-25-01

Problem: She had a detached retina of the left eye last year and now is nearly completely blind in that eye.

Reading: Her eye is lacking a vitamin—either A or E. If she would take high levels of this vitamin under the guidance of a naturopath or physician, her left eye would respond to it.

F 54 yrs 10-18-01

Problem: She has had dry eyes for 15 years. Eye drops do not help, and doctors do not know what to do for her. She has had much stress in her personal life.

Reading: Her pituitary gland is the cause of her dry eyes. It is not releasing enough hormone, and it is stress-related. She should seek treatment for her pituitary gland, which should improve her eye problems.

FATIGUE/LOW ENERGY

F 42 yrs 02-29-99
Problem: She has a low energy level.
Reading: Her neck is out of alignment and needs adjustment. The neck has been like this for a long time and is responsible for 30% of her low energy. The other cause of her low energy is exposure to chemicals.

M 50 yrs 06-19-00
Problem: He has had low energy for 5 years. Recently he was diagnosed with a benign tumor on his thyroid gland.
Reading: His low energy is linked to his thyroid gland, which developed the tumor because of toxins in his blood. He should drink liquid vegetables to flush his organs and apple cider vinegar to flush his colon. He then needs energy work on his thyroid gland.

F 64 yrs 04-03-00
Problem: She is concerned about her lack of energy.
Reading: Her lack of energy is linked to her heart, which looks sluggish and needs exercise. The fatigue also could be connected to her hormone level, which she should have checked.

F 41 yrs 06-29-99
Problem: She is fatigued all the time.
Reading: Her fatigue can be helped with energy work. She has an energy blockage to the front of her face that runs along the side her cheekbones and back toward her ears. Her diaphragm and lungs need to be opened as well. Belly laughter would help. It has been a long time since she has laughed.

F 55 yrs 04-10-00
Problem: She is fatigued.
Reading: Her fatigue is emotionally linked. She has current issues affecting her emotionally that need to be dealt with first before dealing with her childhood issues. She needs energy work in her chest and lower neck. However, she likely will not get behind these challenges.

M 40 yrs 01-24-99
Problem: He feels exhausted most of the time.
Reading: His lack of energy is diet-related, not an energy block. He needs to avoid sugar, caffeine, and chocolate.

F 52 yrs 06-29-99
Problem: She has a low energy level. She becomes weak and often cannot get out of bed. She has been told that she has fibromyalgia.
Reading: She does not have fibromyalgia. Her energy problems are a result of low levels of vitamins and minerals and a lack of consistency in her sleep. Sometimes she can sleep, and other times she cannot. The stress in her life in 1993 took a physical toll that she is still getting over.

F 44 yrs 10-11-99
Problem: She has low energy and life-long depression. She has been in therapy for the depression and takes an antidepressant, but nothing seems to help.
Reading: Her depression began when she was around 3 years of age because of loneliness. The back of her head needs energy work. It has been shut down since she was 3. Her low level of energy is caused by her depression. She needs to see a therapist who will help her cope with her loneliness. Smoking contributes negatively to her depression.

F 44 yrs 06-29-99
Problem: She is frequently tired and believes that it might be caused by a cat allergy. She had a motorcycle accident 30 years ago in which she landed on her head.

Reading: Energy is blocked to one side of the neck up under the jaw, along the side of her face, and across the eye and ear. Energy work to this area will eliminate the fatigue and perhaps help the allergies. One side of her occipital area is locked, and her head is tilted on its axis. This area needs a chiropractic adjustment.

F 28 yrs 10-22-99
Problem: She has had gastrointestinal problems for 3 years. Since then she has had low energy and frequent colds, flu, and strep throats.
Reading: Her colon is the main cause of the low energy, flu, and colds. She needs to start with a colonic enema and then have reflexology and herbs for the digestion. She may have a parasite or a blood disorder. Her blood looks dark red and thick and lacks oxygen. Her blood needs to be looked at as a secondary issue.

F 42 yrs 07-26-98
Problem: She is very tired and has had a lot of stress over the past 5 years. Her muscles also tire quickly.
Reading: She carries a large part of her stress in her jaw and neck muscles. She needs to work on relaxing these areas, and then the body will not tire as quickly. The tiredness in her muscles is linked to joint pain. She needs adjustments in the affected joints as well as vitamins and minerals (particularly potassium). Yoga and yogic breathing also would help her.

F 57 yrs 10-06-98
Problem: She has a low level of energy and difficulty losing weight.
Reading: One side of her body bothers her more than the other. This is caused by a major energy blockage. This blockage runs from the top side of her face straight down through the left hip and stops at the top of the leg. This blockage is partially the reason that she holds her weight and has such a low level of energy. (She then said that she had been involved in an accident and had lost feeling in the left side of her body.) If this blockage is not corrected, she will begin to see a slow, gradual

decline in the left side of the body. She needs energy work to reverse this blockage.

F 28 yrs 10-09-00

Problem: She is very fatigued.

Reading: She has an energy blockage shaped like a horseshoe that starts at the center of her head and runs downward behind the ears and angles forward down to the base of the neck. This shutting down of energy was caused by an injury, not by stress. (She then revealed that she fell out of a car at 2 years of age.) She needs reflexology and Rolfing for the cranial area. About 60% to 70% of her fatigue is caused by the head and neck injury and subsequent energy block. Exhausted adrenals are responsible for the other 30% to 40%.

M 57 yrs 01-22-01

Problem: He was diagnosed with fibromyalgia last year. The treatments worked, but he still lacks energy.

Reading: His fibromyalgia was most likely misdiagnosed, which is why his health appeared to make a quick turn around. His heart looks good, but the lower part is slightly sluggish, which is why he is tired. He should lie on a reclining board (head lower than the feet), drink apple cider vinegar, and partake in cardiovascular exercises. His lungs have some scarring, which has reduced the amount of oxygen in his blood and is another factor contributing to his fatigue.

F 65 yrs 02-02-01

Problem: She feels very "burned out." She has been traveling a lot and believes that this may be the cause. She also has back pain.

Reading: Her hormones release very slowly into her body, and she is a little below her optimal hormone level as well. If her hormone level is raised, her back pain and tiredness will improve. Cardiovascular exercises will improve her hormone level and energy. Energy blockages to both sides of her head and another blockage that runs through the center of her heart valves are also contributing to her tiredness. She is an artist, and the paints with which she works have added to this block-age, but they are not putting her at risk for more serious problems.

F 39 yrs 01-20-01

Problem: She is tired and lacks energy. She is being treated with vita-mins and herbs and is feeling a little better after treatment.

Reading: Her nervous system is the issue, and she should see a neu-rologist for an opinion. Two dark lines running up from the temples to the top of her head do not meet together. This is likely a nerve problem in the brain. She should try reflexology for 60 days. If she shows no improvement, she should then try acupuncture. With daily treatments, she should see a 40% improvement. However, she will have this disor-der for the rest of her life and will need treatments for the rest of her life. She needs to decrease the amount of vitamins that she is taking to avoid harming her liver. Taking them in liquid form may be better.

F 74 yrs 06-10-01

Problem: She has spells of extreme fatigue and weakness while exert-ing or walking and can barely get back home. She has a lot of stress in her marriage and wonders if her emotions could be causing this prob-lem. Medical tests have all come back normal, and doctors have been unable to diagnose her condition.

Reading: She has an inner ear problem and should see an ear specialist. (She then stated that she has extremely sensitive ears and noises bother her. She can even hear neighbors talking while she is inside her home.) A nerve in her ear becomes stimulated by noise. It in turn transfers this stimulation to the portion of the brain that controls motor functions, and she becomes instantly weak.

M 50 yrs 06-11-01

Problem: He recently turned 50 years of age and wants a general health reading. He is an occasional smoker and has undergone a lot of stress during the past 15 years.

Reading: His head is tilted forward and down, which is blocking en-ergy to the frontal portions of the brain, forehead, one side of his face, and his hypothalamus gland. This is causing him to be fatigued. Smoking is contributing to the energy shutdown to his forehead and face. The thymus gland has energy blockage as well. He would benefit from Rolfing and cranial work to the head to move it back and centered properly over the neck. His neck should be Rolfed as well.

F 42 yrs 06-18-01
Problem: Two years ago she began having symptoms of fatigue so great that her arms felt like rubber. She was also light-headed and weak with a sensation of pressure in her head. Doctors suggested that she may have an allergy problem, but she disagrees. Her symptoms are severe one day and slight the next.
Reading: The problem is most likely her reproductive hormones kicking off and on. (She said that 6 months earlier she had had a dilation and curettage [D&C] and now her menstrual periods are back to normal.) She will probably experience heavy bleeding and weakness again within the next year or so, but then she will enter menopause and her periods and fatigue and weakness will go away. For now she should have her hormone levels checked.

F 74 yrs 07-09-01
Problem: She has been very fatigued for the past 2 years, but she feels better after a nap. Doctors believe that she might have fibromyalgia.
Reading: She does have a light case of fibromyalgia brought on by stress, which has affected the adrenal glands and lymphatic system in her chest and upper body. Stress is putting demands on the chemicals released from her brain, probably the endorphins, and this is causing the fatigue. She must learn to control the stress, which also can be treated with acupuncture. The adrenal glands and endorphins can be treated internally with supplements, and the adrenal glands can have acupuncture as well. The lymphatic problem can be treated with massage to the arms, shoulders, and chest.

M 55 yrs 08-16-01
Problem: Since a hernia operation last year, he has been very fatigued

and has had difficulty concentrating. He gets acupuncture treatments, which have helped.

Reading: The hernia surgery has not caused his fatigue, an energy blockage has. He has a block from the clavicles that runs at a 45-degree angle down through his chest and digestive organs and into his groin. His stomach is draining him of energy the most. He should increase his digestion with herbs and digestive enzymes and have acupuncture to the stomach, lungs, and groin. He feels uncertain about his future and abilities, and his emotions have caused this block. Apple cider vinegar would help his stomach and energy. Because his blood is slightly low in minerals such as potassium, it would help his blood as well.

FIBROMYALGIA

F 42 yrs 11-03-99

Problem: She was diagnosed with fibromyalgia 15 years ago. She is always tired.

Reading: Most of her pain is physical, not emotional. It would be good for a nephrologist to look at her kidneys. This is a partial reason for her illness. Her body is reacting to an exposure to chemicals. (She then stated that when she was 21 years of age she was exposed to film processing chemicals and her facial skin broke out in boils.) Her liver and pancreas need to be treated with acupuncture and herbs. Her kidneys were the first to feel the effects of the chemicals. She will see a 60% improvement over the next 2 to 3 years.

F 52 yrs 06-29-99

Problem: She was told that she has fibromyalgia. She becomes weak and often cannot get out of bed. Her energy level is low.

Reading: She does not have fibromyalgia. Her energy problems are linked to low vitamins and minerals and lack of consistency in her sleep. Sometimes she can sleep, and other times she cannot. The stress in her life in 1993 took a physical toll that she is still getting over.

F 38 yrs 01-07-00

Problem: She has fibromyalgia and severe body pain, which increase with inclement weather. She is taking medication and herbs for pain and sleep problems but has to care for her two young children. She has been diagnosed with lupus and has a history of several car accidents.
Reading: The car accidents are the main cause of her health problems. The lupus is not as serious as the fibromyalgia, which is well advanced. She needs emotional work, physical exercise, yoga, breathing exercises, and to do activities that are fun for her. Acupuncture would not help.

F 51 yrs 02-09-01

Problem: She requested a general reading.
Reading: Her pituitary gland is causing a hormone imbalance. She is sensitive to touch on her body and is borderline for fibromyalgia. Balancing her hormones, focusing on those governed by the pituitary gland, can prevent the fibromyalgia. Stress has caused the pituitary problem.

F 68 yrs 03-05-01

Problem: She has severe neck and back pain, and doctors want to implant a morphine pump in her lower back. The neck injury occurred in a car accident and the back injury in a fall. She has had neck surgery and three lower back surgeries. Ten years ago she was diagnosed with fibromyalgia. She also has low energy and is very tired.
Reading: The fibromyalgia was either misdiagnosed or very mild. She has a nerve problem that seems to be coming from her neck that runs down her leg to the big toe. (She says that this is correct.) The thymus gland may be affected as well and is partially causing the pain. Her body pain results from the neck and thymus gland problems.

F 56 yrs 04-28-01

Problem: She was diagnosed with fibromyalgia 8 years ago for which she is taking medication. The pain is mainly in her neck and upper back, although it involves her entire body. She also has numbness in her fingers and hands, right foot, and left heel, which began after she fell and broke her foot. This numbness has been diagnosed as a neuropathy.

Reading: Her cranium has moved forward slightly, and this is interfering with a gland–likely the hypothalamus–in the front portion of her brain. When questioned whether she has had head trauma or headaches, she said that she sees flashing lights. This was diagnosed as ocular migraine, and she was told not to worry about it. This gland cannot function properly and is the reason for the fibromyalgia, the numbness, and the flashing in her vision. Cranial massage would help move the cranium. Then she should have acupuncture to stimulate the hypothalamus.

F 61 yrs 06-11-01

Problem: She has been told that she has had fibromyalgia for 24 years. She gets dizzy and weak and has vision and memory problems. She has seen many doctors, had hands-on healing, and talked to psychics and shamans, yet no one has been able to help her.

Reading: She has an energy block starting at the upper lip, which extends through the brainstem and runs through the neck and spinal cord and out through the arms and hands. Something frightened her when she was a young teenager, and this ultimately manifested as a fear in her as an adult. This has caused the fibromyalgia and is worse from the waist up. She needs energy work starting with the upper lip and working backward.

F 74 yrs 07-09-01

Problem: The muscle in her arms and wrists have begun to ache for the past few months, and she now has small lumps between the knuckle joints on the fingers of her left hand. She has also been very fatigued for the past 2 years, but she feels better after a nap. Doctors believe that she might have fibromyalgia.

Reading: She does have a light case of fibromyalgia brought on by stress, which has affected the adrenal glands and lymphatic system in her chest and upper body. Stress is putting demands on the chemicals released from her brain, probably the endorphins, and this is causing the fatigue and muscle pain. She must learn to control the stress, which also can be treated with acupuncture. The adrenal glands and endorphins can be treated internally with supplements, and the adrenal glands can have acupuncture as well. The lymphatic problem can be treated with massage to the arms, shoulders, and chest.

F 43 yrs 09-09-01

Problem: She was diagnosed with fibromyalgia 10 years ago and is sometimes bedridden for 4 days at a time. Every day she has pain and fatigue and is sensitive all over her body, particularly in her joints and neck. She is on an antidepressant for the fibromyalgia and is trying to cope with the chronic pain.

Reading: Her past relationship caused this problem because she did not feel cared about, and because no one cared, she became ill. She has not figured out how to cope with the fibromyalgia, so she has decided to join it rather than fight it. She needs the emotional and spiritual side of her treated first. She has an energy block from the gallbladder to the liver to the spleen, and she needs energy work there. The antidepressant does not seem to be beneficial to these organs, and their dysfunction is the reason for her joint pain. Caffeine and foods high in acid are also affecting the fibromyalgia. She needs to learn to fight this disease. Some psychotherapy or self-motivational tapes would help. Yoga, relaxation, or deep breathing also would be beneficial.

F 63 yrs 10-11-01

Problem: She was diagnosed with fibromyalgia and has had 8 years of chronic body pain. Her legs are her biggest problem—she can only walk a few steps at a time. She has a rare red blood cell (RBC) disorder, and doctors believe that this is causing her leg problems. She is also very fatigued and unable to work because of her condition.

Reading: The lining of her lungs looks irregular, as though she were exposed to a chemical burn or smoke inhalation. This caused her lungs not to filter blood properly and resulted in her blood being poisoned. The blood passing through the digestive tract is not much better, and by the time it reaches her legs, it is in its worst condition with the RBCs nearly depleted. Her lung condition caused both the RBC disorder and the fibromyalgia. She needs to increase the oxygen levels in her blood. (She then stated that she has been smoking since she was a little girl.)

FOOD INTOLERANCES

F 65 yrs 12-06-98
Problem: She has blood-shot eyes.
Reading: The blood-shot eyes might be caused by food sensitivities.

F 47 yrs 01-28-98
Problem: She believes that she has a major food allergy problem.
Reading: The food sensitivities are not as bad as she or her doctors believe. Some of the food reactions are emotionally related. (She then explained that her father was very abusive at the dinner table, and this apparently still affects her.)

F 40 yrs 10-05-98
Problem: She thinks that she has food allergies.
Reading: She is intolerant of four food types. The food intolerances bother her eyes, stomach, and colon. She needs to drink a lot more water and watch the carbohydrate consumption. She should drink water

when she eats. (She said that she never drinks water with a meal.) The spots on her face are linked to a combination of high stress and eating one of the four foods of which she is intolerant. This combination causes this reaction.

F 73 yrs 09-05-99

Problem: She has had a chronic cough for 30 years. She has seen an allergist for her cough, but it has not helped. She is taking a blood pressure medication.

Reading: She needs to pay more attention to her diet. Her cough is related to food sensitivity, mostly to sugar and salt, and she needs to be tested for other food intolerances. If she cuts back on fats and salt, she will have less need for the blood pressure medication.

M 7 yrs 09-27-99

Problem: He has seemed angry since birth. He has to be told to do things several times, and does not do what he is told. He is sensitive and cries a lot. He is prone to strep throats.

Reading: He does not have a mental disorder; his behavior is diet-related. He has a lot of congestion in his forehead and chronic headaches because of the pressure. His parents should watch his intake of processed foods, milk, cheese, sugar, and salt. He is sensitive to the processed foods, and the others are giving him the congestion. If the diet does not work, he could have acupuncture and energy work. The strep throats will go away when his diet improves.

F 37 yrs 05-08-00

Problem: She has had headaches for the past 12 years.

Reading: She has a food intolerance–probably to green vegetables.

F 25 yrs 04-03-00

Problem: She has migraine headaches several times a year.

Reading: Her migraine headaches are diet-related and triggered by caffeine and dairy. Red meat contributes to her weight gain.

F 43 yrs 01-10-00

Problem: She has been told that she has a thyroid condition.

Reading: Her thyroid gland looks sensitive to fats and yeast. The outside lobes look the most irritated. Acupuncture to the thyroid gland would help. Also, her stomach acid level looks high, and at times she suffers from stomach problems. She should avoid acidic foods.

F 54 yrs 03-18-01

Problem: She has wheat intolerance.

Reading: Her breathing is very shallow, and this is causing inadequate levels of blood and oxygen in the digestive system after eating to enable proper digestion of wheat (or any other food for that matter). As the food begins to dissolve she has an easier time digesting because at that point not as much oxygen is required as in the earlier stages of digestion. She is suppressing her emotions, which is suppressing her diaphragm. She needs to learn diaphragmatic breathing or take up yoga. She also should work on the issue from her early childhood that caused the shallow breathing.

F 57 yrs 02-20-01

Problem: She has wheat intolerance, among other food sensitivities. Diagnostic tests have shown that she has high, toxic levels of metals in her system.

Reading: The back, upper portion of her brain has been exposed to chemicals, most likely oil-based chemicals and lead. (She then stated that she is an artist.) These likely are the metals showing up as toxic levels in her system. The wheat intolerance is caused by this chemical exposure. She should see a naturopathic physician for herbs that would cleanse her system of these metals.

M 9 yrs 02-24-01

Problem: He is hot-tempered, fears the dark, is dyslexic, defecates in his pants, and has the speech pattern of a 5 year old. He eats a lot of bread and cheese, his favorite foods. The chiropractor has put him on homeopathic medications because he is toxic and has parasites.

Reading: Rather than having a parasite or high toxic level problem, he has food intolerances, with dairy being the greatest problem. He is also intolerant of wheat and yeast. These foods are affecting his gallbladder, and he will have gallstones if he does not make a dietary change. The pituitary and adrenal glands are causing these food intolerances and need to be treated to control his cravings for these foods. Reflexology to the pituitary and adrenal glands and gallbladder would be good. He also is retaining water because of his adrenal glands and this in turn is causing his body to retain salt. His low tolerance of these foods is causing his dyslexia and impaired speech pattern.

F 41 yrs 07-02-01

Problem: Her lungs are in poor health because she is around fiberglass and cigarette smoke. She has asthma and uses an inhaler off and on. She has bronchitis frequently and takes antibiotics periodically as well. She also takes allergy medications. If she stays on her lung medications she only becomes ill three to six times per year. She is also tired and overweight (she gained 80 pounds in the past year), has headaches lasting several days, had part of her thyroid gland removed 8 years ago, and is on antidepression medication. For nearly a year she has had a breakout of reddish boils with pus, which has been diagnosed as folliculitis.

Reading: Her body does not like dairy products, and this is affecting her circulation and clogging her pores, thus causing the skin boils. The bronchioles of the lungs are worse than the lungs themselves. The dairy and the poor circulation are contributing to the lung problems and weight gain and affecting the sinuses. The antidepressant is not helping but is contributing to her fatigue and straining her liver. It is also slowing her digestive process and contributing to her weight gain. She should try a natural antidepressant. Eliminating dairy is the most important approach to her health. Acupuncture to her lungs, bronchioles, liver, small intestine, and thyroid gland would help as well.

FOOT/ANKLE PROBLEMS

F 53 yrs 01-10-00
Problem: The bottom of her foot has a sharp pain that comes and goes.
Reading: The bottom of the foot looks like it has scar tissue that has formed and interfered with the nerves. Pain occurs when she applies pressure to the foot. Corrective shoes would help, as would increasing her potassium intake.

F 74 yrs 10-25-99
Problem: She has left ankle pain that is eluding the doctors
Reading: The problem is a ligament that runs up the calf. Acupuncture would help.

F 60 yrs 03-03-98
Problem: Her left heel is sore and tender, more so when she gets up in the morning.
Reading: The cause of the heel pain is uneven distribution of weight. The shinbone, particularly the area just below the knee, is or was strained, and this leg to the front and back of the knee has become weak. The weakness then caused her to plant her foot down unevenly when walking or standing. After a time, this action has taken its toll on the heel and it has become inflamed. The inflammation increases throughout the day and while she is sleeping. When she bears weight on it in the morning, it is like pressing down on a large blister. Icing the heel before going to bed would yield an improvement in the mornings. Perhaps aspirin or an antiinflammatory would help for a while if her physician agrees.

F 52 yrs 12-13-98

Problem: The arches of her feet are sore and achy.

Reading: She bears more weight on the front portion of her feet. This is putting a strain on the arches, which "fall" when her feet are tired. She needs to wear a good running shoe and arch supports in her other shoes.

M 33 yrs 05-06-97

Problem: The balls of his feet are tender, one foot more so than the other.

Reading: His feet are aging more quickly than normal. The inside arches and the bottoms of the toes are also tender. This problem is stomach-related—he has a high level of stomach acid. He should wear better support shoes and avoid citrus foods.

F 42 yrs 07-26-98

Problem: The ball of her left foot and her right hip hurt.

Reading: Her hip problem aggravates the ball of her foot. The hip ligaments are tight, and the hip needs an adjustment. She needs to do stretching exercises. She also needs vitamin and mineral supplements, minerals more than vitamins, particularly potassium. She should let her body catch up to her mind. Her mind has improved in its healing, but the body has not moved at the same rate. Yoga and yogic breathing would help.

M 48 yrs 07-12-99

Problem: His feet bother him. The muscles or tendons in his feet are inflamed, and he has been told that he has pronation (leans to one side when standing) and bursitis. One doctor wants him to take cortisone and stay off his feet for 5 months. He wears support pads in his shoes. He drank heavily for 20 years, although he has not had any alcohol in 5 years.

Reading: His problem is linked to the uric acid in his blood. He should be tested for gout. The high uric acid has also affected his hands and wrists.

F 73 yrs 03-10-01
Problem: Her feet became paralyzed 1 year ago, but MRI and x-ray examinations are negative. She is now incontinent of urine and lacks bladder control.
Reading: Her bladder control and foot condition are caused by her adrenal glands. She needs to see an endocrinologist. Her hormone level has affected her neurologic system. She has too much salt in her system because her adrenal glands are causing water retention, and this is affecting her bladder.

GUM/TOOTH PROBLEMS

F 43 yrs 02-21-99
Problem: Her gums have been deteriorating over the last 10 years.
Reading: Her gum problem is caused mostly by a mineral deficiency. She needs to increase her mineral intake.

F 38 yrs 12-02-99
Problem: She has a painful tooth abscess. She wants to know if her root canal is infected or if her tooth needs to be pulled.
Reading: She has a minor infection for which she may need an antibiotic. Pulling the tooth is not the answer; the gums need to be treated instead. Her gums and teeth have a mineral deficiency, so she needs to increase her mineral intake. Also, the pituitary gland looks exhausted, which is a factor in her gum problem. Learning to relax and meditate will help her pituitary gland.

F 41 yrs 10-17-99
Problem: She has had gum and tooth inflammation for the past week.
Reading: The tooth and gum problem is energy-related. She has an energy blockage that starts 2 inches above her navel and runs up through the base of her head and down through the back of the neck into the trapezius muscles. This energy blockage is stress-related. The order of treatment should be therapy for her emotional state, energy work to clear the blockage, and acupuncture.

F 38 yrs 12-15-99
Problem: She had a toothache 3 weeks ago. The dentist treated her, and when the pain returned she was told that nothing is wrong. Two years ago her ear swelled to twice its size. After taking antibiotics, she was then treated with acupuncture, which helped the pain temporarily, but the pain returned. Doctors believe that she has symptoms of multiple sclerosis. She is on an antiepilepsy medication, which has helped the pain. She wants to know if her body is fighting cancer.
Reading: She does not have cancer or multiple sclerosis. A germ or bacteria in the blood has settled in her jaw. She likely had an open sore and the bacteria entered her mouth at that time. (She then stated that she has gum recession at the canine teeth, which is where the pain has been.) This is the site at which the bacteria entered the blood stream.

HAIR LOSS

F 74 yrs 10-25-98
Problem: She is losing her hair and has been told that it is stress-related.
Reading: Her hair loss is stress-related but not to the point that she

cannot control it. She is deficient in vitamins, and her hair and scalp are dry. She needs to use a mild or natural shampoo and avoid shampooing every day. Her hair products should contain extra oils. Eating according to her blood type may help as well.

F 56 yrs 03-13-00
Problem: She is losing her hair, and her cholesterol level is high.
Reading: The hair loss is linked to her high cholesterol level.

F 41 yrs 06-29-99
Problem: She is losing her hair.
Reading: Her hair loss is stress-related. She needs to laugh. It would yield long-term benefits.

M 30 yrs 07-08-00
Problem: He began losing his hair at around 15 or 16 years of age and wants to know the cause.
Reading: His diet is an important factor in his hair loss. He needs B vitamins and to avoid fried foods. Also, his liver is toxic and is another link to his hair loss. Selenium would be good for age spots and his toxic liver. He should drink apple cider vinegar.

F 74 yrs 02-16-01
Problem: She has been losing her hair for 40 years and has been diagnosed with alopecia, although she still has her eyebrows and eyelashes. Doctors do not know the cause.
Reading: Her low red blood cell (RBC) count is the cause of her alopecia, and her liver causes the blood cell problem. Reflexology or acupuncture to the liver likely would raise her RBC count. Stress has caused the liver problem, and acupuncture treatments for stress may help as well.

M 44 yrs 04-15-01
Problem: He is losing his hair, and his body temperature is lower than

normal. Doctors at first believed that he had a hypothyroid condition, but tests have shown his thyroid to be normal.

Reading: His blood looks a little thick and shows high levels of nicotine, alcohol, and caffeine. He is not a smoker, but he is in a room full of smoke every day. (He states that he is a welder and is around exhaust all day long.) He is breathing these gases into his lungs, which is affecting his blood and the pores in his head. This is an environmental problem and is also causing the hair loss. He needs to wear a hat and better facemask when he is working around cars, get more sunlight for his head, drink pure water, and breathe pure air. He also needs to perform breathing exercises. His lungs are clogged and dirty and need to be cleansed. His lungs are the cause of his low body temperature as well.

F 27 yrs 04-05-99
Problem: Recently she has been losing a lot of hair.
Reading: Her liver is toxic, and the pituitary gland is exhausted. She needs help in dealing with stress, such as hypnosis. Her brain is releasing (or overproducing) minerals, most likely a result of the pituitary gland being stressed and in need of restoration. She needs reflexology to treat the pituitary gland, pancreas, and liver. The hair loss is linked to the problems with her pituitary gland.

HEADACHES/MIGRAINES

F 53 yrs 12-03-99
Problem: She has migraine headaches and mood swings. She is on hormone replacement therapy and believes that her mood swings are connected to her menstrual periods.

Reading: She is angry and unhappy and has been for some time. Her migraine headaches are connected to the anger and are soft-tissue–related (tightness of the cranial and occipital muscles). She is spiritually weak and not well grounded. Prayer will help her relax and be more focused.

F 51 yrs 10-19-98

Problem: She has headaches at the back of her head. She also has muscle spasms and back pain. She wonders if her headaches are migraines.

Reading: Her headaches are caused by muscle spasms in her neck. A chiropractor should fix the main problem first (upper middle back between the shoulders). After this area has been fixed, the neck and lower back will respond to treatment much better.

F 35 yrs 01-11-99

Problem: She has migraine headaches and has been treated with herbs, acupuncture, and Rolfing.

Reading: Rolfing will help more than acupuncture for her migraine headaches, which is an energy problem. Treatments have not helped to the degree that one would expect. The herbs have helped with the depression in a psychological way because she believes so strongly in them. The energy blockage that is causing her problems starts at the top of the forehead on one side and runs at a 45-degree angle across the forehead over one eye, down the side of the neck, and into the upper right chest. The second major blockage starts at the back of the head. It runs down the back of her neck, through the center of the shoulder blades, and moves to the center of the spine between the shoulders. She has opened energy at the top of her head that runs straight down through the center of her head and front of her body. This energy is strong and is preventing the front half of her body from connecting with the back half of her body, and this has increased the migraines. She needs energy work in the areas described. After the energy work, her body will come together and heal.

F 41 yrs 06-29-99

Problem: She has frequent headaches.

Reading: Her headaches can be helped with energy work. She has an energy blockage to the front of her face that runs along the side of her cheekbones, back toward her ears. Her diaphragm and lungs need to be opened as well.

F 25 yrs 04-03-00

Problem: She has migraine headaches several times a year.

Reading: Her migraine headaches are diet-related, particularly to caffeine and dairy products.

F 23 yrs 02-26-98

Problem: She has headaches and migraine headaches. Her mother reports that she has poor eating habits.

Reading: The top center of her head is blocked, and energy is not getting through. If this blockage were to open, it would help her migraine headaches. Her migraines are not food-related. Skipping breakfast and other eating habits are not the problem. Her daily stress would not affect her if her energy were not blocked. She needs to meditate and do mild exercises (e.g., yoga or tai chi) but avoid heavy exercises.

M 33 yrs 05-06-97

Problem: He has headaches that start high on the forehead and extend downward to the eyebrows.

Reading: He needs to wear good sunglasses. Glare from the sun is irritating his eyes and may be the cause of some of the headaches, but not all of them. His neck and shoulder muscles and deltoids are weak, and the upper chest muscles are tight. Push-ups and upper body exercises would help him.

F 26 yrs 03-26-96

Problem: She has migraine headaches.

Reading: Although the migraine headaches will continue and be difficult to prevent, exercise would help a lot and could be the mainstay in preventing them.

F 50 yrs 03-27-96

Problem: She has headaches high on her forehead and over and under one eye.

Reading: The bridge of her nose and cheekbone appear to have been injured in an accident. The tendons or muscles are very tight on the front of her neck, where they attach to the base of the chest. The back of her neck, three-quarters of the way down, appears to be irritated by the tight tendons. Two vertebrae between the shoulder blades are displaced. (After the reading she stated that she had been in a car accident in which her face hit the steering wheel.) She needs massage therapy and Rolfing. Her face and head need to be massaged first, then the neck and upper back.

F 21 yrs 10-27-96

Problem: She has frequent headaches across her forehead.

Reading: The headaches are caused by too much contemplation. She is too analytical. She needs to exercise the body more and the mind less.

F 43 yrs 02-21-99

Problem: She has dull headaches, a lack of focus, and an inability to sleep long enough at night.

Reading: The headaches, lack of focus, and sleep problem are all related to her low mineral level. She needs zinc, potassium, and other minerals in general.

F 47 yrs 09-13-99

Problem: She has migraine headaches.

Reading: She has a nerve or energy flow disorder that starts at the top of her forehead and runs down across the right cheek to the base of the neck. She will have pain or discomfort on the right side of her face, and the migraine headache will occur on the next day. Although dairy products are not the cause of the migraine, they do contribute to the level of the migraine that she experiences. Therefore she should avoid cheese, ice cream, and milk. Acupuncture would be good for restoring energy flow.

F 39 yrs 02-21-00
Problem: She has had headaches for the last 7 months.
Reading: She has a lymphatic disorder in the base of her neck near the clavicle. First she eats foods that form toxins, then the blocked lymph node prevents the toxins from moving out of the body and ultimately the brain, and this causes the headaches. She needs a lymphatic treatment such as massage. She should also eat according to her blood type. This will diminish the toxins and improve the headaches within 3 months.

F 37 yrs 05-08-00
Problem: She has had headaches for the past 12 years.
Reading: She has a food intolerance–probably to green vegetables. She should have a food sensitivity test that focuses on green vegetables.

F 47 yrs 09-20-99
Problem: She has migraine headaches.
Reading: She has two abnormal points on her back that would benefit from acupuncture–the upper middle back on the left side and the lumbar area on the right side. (Her doctor confirms that after treating her with acupuncture, she no longer has tenderness in those areas and has not had a migraine headache since the treatment.)

F 45 yrs 10-30-00
Problem: She gets migraine headaches around the time of her periods.
Reading: Eating chocolates triggers her migraine headaches.

M 77 yrs 02-26-01
Problem: He has had continuous headaches for 15 years since having had a car accident. He had laser surgery to the brainstem that relieved 50% of his neck pain.
Reading: The headaches, which resemble migraines, are caused by

tight cranial muscles that are restricting blood flow through the veins in the back and side of his head. Acupuncture to these areas may be a viable treatment. He should also apply hot, moist heat to help alleviate the headaches.

M 56 yrs 06-02-01

Problem: He fell from the roof of his house 20 years ago and has had headaches since then. They can last for 5 days at a time. The side of his head that he sleeps on is the side in which the headache occurs. His head feels as though it is on fire, and his skull is hot to the touch. Neurologic tests have all been negative. Diet, alcohol, fans, and breezes can trigger a headache. After the injury he had acupuncture for 6 years, which helped because before that he could not hold his head up.

Reading: The headaches and burning in his head are caused by a lack of oxygen to his brain. Vertebrae in his thoracic spine have affected the nerves that control the lungs. Acupuncture and energy work help because they open energy and oxygen flow. When he stops, the problem returns. For more lasting results he should have his neck, upper thorax, and lungs worked on rather than his head.

F 30 yrs 07-21-01

Problem: She began getting migraine headaches when she was 12 years of age. For the past 4 years she has been getting them five to six times a week, and they last for 18 to 24 hours. She becomes nauseated and is light-sensitive. Doctors have tried every approach and every form of medication, but the headaches do not go away. MRIs, computed tomography (CT) scans, and electroencephalograms (EEGs) are all negative.

Reading: She does not appear to have a brain disorder. Her problem is toxic blood, and it is coming from the liver. Her ankles and the bottoms of her feet are connected to the migraine headaches in some way. Acupuncture for her liver and reflexology to her feet would help her.

F 7 yrs 07-21-01

Problem: She has had nausea and a headache over her right eyebrow for the past year. She complains constantly about not feeling well. She has difficulty going to sleep and waking up. She prefers not to talk or express herself. One year ago she fell out of a bunk bed and struck her face. Doctors do not believe that this accident is connected to her headache.

Reading: Her problems were caused by trauma, and falling out of bed appears to be the likely event. Doctors have not found the problem because they are focusing on her head and brain while the problem centers around her neck, shoulders, and chest. The atlas at her first cervical vertebra is rotated, and her head is twisted to the side and not balanced on her neck and shoulders. This is interfering with the nerves in her neck and shoulders and causing the headaches. Several pressure points and nerves in her upper chest, back, shoulders, diaphragm, and clavicle need to be treated. First she needs Rolfing to these areas and then acupuncture.

M 44 yrs 10-05-01

Problem: He has had headaches every morning for 15 years, but they are gone by the time he goes to sleep. Every 3 months he has a migraine headache. The morning headaches last 2 to 3 hours each and are in the back of his skull. CT scan, MRI, and other tests are negative. Sometimes his ears turn bright red when he has these headaches.

Reading: The headaches are kidney-related. Kidney pressure changes during the night while he is lying in bed. The kidneys should be treated with acupuncture, and a chiropractor might treat the area of the back that controls kidney function. He also needs to watch his salt intake because it is altering pressure in his kidneys.

HEARTBEAT, IRREGULAR

M 55 yrs 01-28-98
Problem: He has had recent chest discomfort and is concerned about his heart.
Reading: His heart is okay. He needs to cut back on caffeine intake. The caffeine is stimulating his heart and contributing to a narrowing of the arteries, which is causing his heart to have a rapid beat.

F 66 yrs 03-19-98
Problem: She has an irregular heartbeat for which she has been taking medication for 32 years.
Reading: Her heart does not look bad–she has a problem with circulation. Blood is not adequately getting through from the upper half of the body to the lower half. Perhaps the altered blood supply to her heart is the cause of the irregular heartbeat. She needs to have the main vein in her neck checked, as well as the circulation to her heart, groin, and leg. Although this is not serious, it is the main cause of her problem.

F 78 yrs 03-08-99
Problem: She has heart palpitations. An MRI was negative.
Reading: She does not have a major nerve or circulation problem, although the lower valves in her heart are weaker than the upper valves. Her main problem is her blood, which is low in minerals–particularly potassium and sodium. She should see a naturopath for minerals.

F 27 yrs 05-01-00
Problem: She was diagnosed with a hyperthyroid condition. She gets

the shakes and feels her heart beating too fast. Recently she broke off her engagement and has been told that she must get rid of her dogs.

Reading: The rapid heart rate is connected to the thyroid gland, and both are linked to stress. Her occipital area looks off center, which is causing one side of her neck to pull at the base, twisting the neck muscles and affecting the center and upper lobes of her thyroid gland. Nothing is physically wrong with the heart; the heart rate is emotionally driven. The thyroid gland looks normal; it is just currently very active. If she works on her stress, her thyroid gland may return to normal. Acupuncture would help.

F 48 yrs 02-03-01

Problem: She has an irregular heartbeat (premature ventricular contractions [PVCs]). She has been diagnosed with hepatitis C.

Reading: Although her aorta has been affected by the hepatitis, a greater concern for her heart is her hormonal deficiency. (She concurs that she goes through her menstrual cycles but does not produce any blood.) Her aorta looks dark and has energy blockage. She needs energy work to her aorta, and then she will have fewer PVCs.

M 43 yrs 04-16-01

Problem: For the past 7 months he has experienced a rapid heart rate of 130 to 140 beats per minute when at rest. Diagnostic tests have all been negative. His doctor told him that he was not at risk and to exercise. A cardiac specialist put him on a beta blocker. He was born with asthma but discontinued the asthma medication because a vitamin C, oat tablet, and copper pill have kept his asthma in check for the past 3 years.

Reading: His lungs may be the cause of his racing heart. They appear to have blood boils or small pockets of blood that rupture and drain back into the heart. When this happens, the rapid heart rate is triggered. Discontinuing his asthma medication likely has caused the formation of the blood pockets. If he continues to use the asthma inhaler, the irregular heart rate will go away. Acupuncture of the lungs also would be helpful for him.

F 55 yrs 03-26-01
Problem: She has had heart palpitations for 2 years. She wears an estrogen patch.
Reading: The patch that she is wearing is not strong enough for later in the day when she becomes tired and stressed. The heart palpitations are both stress-and hormone-related.

HEARTBURN

M 55 yrs 01-28-98
Problem: He has had recent chest discomfort and is concerned about his heart.
Reading: His heart is okay. He has digestive problems, heartburn, and obesity. He needs to cut back on his caffeine and citrus intake. The acid in the caffeine and citrus is causing heartburn.

F 42 yrs 12-11-98
Problem: She has had heartburn since she started taking birth control pills. She wonders if the two are connected.
Reading: The heartburn is very high in the stomach, mostly where the esophagus attaches to the stomach. This irritation can be dealt with by taking over-the-counter medications. The cause is partly stress (70%) and partly dietary (30%). If she relaxes, breathes consciously, and regulates her medication and diet, this stomach problem will go away. The birth control pills did not cause the heartburn in the way that she thinks they do. The stress of worrying about taking the pill has increased her level of acid and has caused the stomach irritation.

M 49 yrs 07-31-00
Problem: He has heartburn.
Reading: Carbonated drinks are bad for him, so he should avoid them.

F 68 yrs 01-06-01
Problem: She has severe heartburn. She also has a lot of job pressure.
Reading: Her heartburn occurs because of her spleen. Reflexology or acupuncture will help her spleen. She should also eat according to her blood type.

HEART (CARDIAC) PROBLEMS

M 46 yrs 11-03-99
Problem: He was diagnosed with "heart troubles."
Reading: He needs cardiovascular and weight-lifting exercises for his heart. His potassium level looks low, and drinking apple cider vinegar would help.

M 60 yrs 02-18-01
Problem: He is concerned about his heart.
Reading: Eating according to his blood type would prevent the development of coronary heart disease.

F 48 yrs 11-03-99
Problem: She was diagnosed with an electrical heart condition 1 year ago. She gets light-headed and pale. She is taking a lot of herbs and heart medications, and doctors want her to take even more.

Reading: A nerve is affecting the upper central valves of her heart. A vertebra in the upper mid-back is most likely the cause. Once this is fixed, the valve will be okay. Acupuncture would be an effective treatment. She also needs yoga or tai chi and to work on emotional and physical problems simultaneously.

F 90 yrs 11-23-98

Problem: She had a recent heart attack, followed by a pacemaker implant. Doctors say that the pacemaker is not controlling the buildup of fluids. She also has low energy.

Reading: The lower heart valve is very weak. Walking would be very good for her, and she should avoid becoming sedentary. She needs sunlight to increase her energy. The build up of fluids is a concern. She should drink plenty of water and vegetable juice to keep her kidneys healthy. Emotionally she is getting tired of the daily struggles. She needs to keep her mind happy with entertainment.

F 56 yrs 03-13-00

Problem: She cannot exercise for as long as she was accustomed to when she was younger.

Reading: She has circulatory problems. Her heart and lungs look weak, and this has created the weak blood flow throughout her body. She needs cardiovascular exercise as well as apple cider vinegar for potassium to help her heart and lungs.

F 51 yrs 01-28-01

Problem: She has had pain near her spleen for the last 5 years. She is very tired and cannot keep her eyes open.

Reading: Her pituitary gland is dripping hormones slowly like a faucet that cannot be turned off. She needs to have pituitary and hormone tests done. Pain near the spleen is caused by her lower heart valves. They are not blocked, but they are not performing properly because of the hormonal dysfunction. Getting more oxygen into the blood would help her heart. Apple cider vinegar could help the heart valves, as well as long walks and lying on a reclining board (head lower than the feet).

Emotions have caused these problems. She has a tendency to think negatively and needs a spiritual reunion with God.

F 45 yrs 06-27-01
Problem: She has been diagnosed as clinically dead four times in her life. She was rushed to the hospital with no pulse 3 weeks ago. The first time it happened she was 29 years of age and cycling on her bike when she passed out after her heart had stopped. Her heart beats quickly and then stops. Doctors say that she has a leaky heart valve but it is not severe enough to warrant surgery. She has had treadmill tests, injections of dye, and workups by eight different heart specialists, but no one has been able to determine what causes her to "die" when her heart stops and then return to life. She had been on many heart medications and blood thinners but now is taking only beta blockers.
Reading: She has a serious adrenal gland disorder. These glands have ceased producing adequate levels of hormones, which immediately affects the pituitary and reproductive glands, temporarily shutting down all body functions and sending the body into shock. She needs to see an endocrinologist. The adrenal glands need to be treated with herbs, acupuncture, and reflexology to determine if this improves the pituitary and reproductive glands, as well as the heart.

HERPESVIRUS

F 66 yrs 01-28-01
Problem: She has kidney problems and a herpesvirus infection.
Reading: A hormone imbalance stemming from the ovaries is causing a rush of hormones through the kidneys and affecting their performance. This may be causing the herpesvirus to stay active. The herpes-

virus is not stress-related but rather physically caused. She should drink apple cider vinegar for the kidneys, and the virus likely will subside. Acupuncture for the kidneys would help as well.

M 60 yrs 06-09-01

Problem: He has herpesvirus infection and it is contributing to his depression.

Reading: His depression and anger is a learned behavior that began around 9 or 10 years of age. His current level of meditation is helping him deal with his current anger but not with the deeper issues of anger from his childhood. For those issues he needs to take his meditation deeper. Psychotherapy would be good for that as well. Also, his liver is toxic, and that is where he carries his anger. Detoxifying his liver would help with his herpesvirus infection.

HORMONAL/CHANGE-OF-LIFE ISSUES

F 43 yrs 11-02-98

Problem: She has been depressed since her full hysterectomy in 1992 and struggles with mental imbalance. She takes estrogen but has gained a lot of weight. She also has an uncontrollable temper at times.

Reading: Her hormones are hard to balance. She needs very small increments in her estrogen dosage to find her optimal hormonal balance.

F 55 yrs 09-13-99
Problem: She wants to know if using a natural hormone will be okay once she begins menopause.
Reading: Her menopause will be a normal one. Using a natural product will be fine.

F 52 yrs 12-13-99
Problem: Her blood pressure is out of control at times.
Reading: Her hormone levels are good, but she needs to switch the brand of synthetic hormone that she is using. It may be causing her blood pressure problem. If switching does not regulate her blood pressure, the dosage of her current brand should be decreased.

F 52 yrs 12-13-98
Problem: She is going through menopause and taking natural progesterone cream for her hormone imbalance. She is having hot flashes.
Reading: She should increase her use of the progesterone cream from once a day to twice a day.

F 56 yrs 11-18-99
Problem: She has a clogged lymph node under one arm and joint stiffness. She is on synthetic hormone replacement therapy. She is also having difficulty losing weight.
Reading: The outer area of her breast has some dark fiber or tough-looking tissue. She should switch to a natural hormone. Her joint pain will subside once she begins using a natural hormone, exercises (cardiovascular and weight training), and eats properly.

F 43 yrs 08-30-99
Problem: She is postmenopausal and is taking estrogen. She has gained 25 pounds and wants to use herbs rather than the estrogen, but they have not worked. Her sex drive is low.
Reading: She should continue taking the estrogen, but it needs to be regulated carefully. She should take it every day at very low dosages and then increase the dose slowly over 5 to 6 months until she finds the

proper balance. She will be surprised that her balance point will be very low. She can try herbs after she achieves estrogen balance. However, her weight problem is 60% thyroid-related and 40% diet-related. She needs to stop eating breads and drink more water. Her thyroid gland is sluggish and needs stimulation. Her bones look soft and she needs calcium and cardiovascular and aerobic exercise. The low sex drive will increase once she achieves the proper hormonal balance.

F 50 yrs 07-09-00
Problem: She is beginning menopause and has low energy. Her job and schooling are stressful.
Reading: Her hormone level is just out of normal range. She has good health entering menopause, and a natural hormone will most likely help. She needs to learn to breathe and relax effectively. Taking St. John's Wort, communicating with her husband, and balancing her hormones are factors in reducing her stress level.

F 57 yrs 09-13-99
Problem: She is in menopause and taking estrogen. She has trouble sleeping if she stops taking the drug, although she wants to and has tried. She bleeds at the end of the month when she stops taking the estrogen, but she bleeds profusely when she takes it.
Reading: She was likely misdiagnosed with a hormone problem in her thirties and was treated for it with synthetic hormones and therefore has had a hormone imbalance problem for the last 20 years. She will now have difficulty finding a hormone balance.

F 53 yrs 12-03-99
Problem: She has high blood pressure. She is on synthetic hormone replacement therapy.
Reading: The high blood pressure is caused by the hormone medication.

F 65 yrs 02-02-01

Problem: She feels "burned out." She has been traveling a lot and believes that this may be the cause. She also has back pain.

Reading: Her hormones release very slowly into her body, and she is a little below her optimal hormone level. If her hormone level were raised, her back pain and fatigue would decrease. Cardiovascular exercises would improve her hormone level and energy. Energy blockages to both sides of her head and another blockage that runs through the center of her heart valves are also contributing to her fatigue. She is an artist, and the paints with which she works have added to this blockage, but they are not putting her at risk for more serious problems.

F 65 yrs 02-17-01

Problem: She had a hysterectomy and since then has had trouble with her hearing, vision, sleeping, and memory. Loud noises bother her, she is exhausted and confused, and she believes that her body is falling apart.

Reading: Her body produced more scar tissue than it should have, both in the sides of her neck and breasts. This has resulted in a lack of blood and oxygen to the brain and can put her at risk for stroke. She needs a boost of hormones to prevent this scar tissue formation. Herbs for the brain would also help her thought processes.

F 61 yrs 10-14-00

Problem: She has an itchy skin rash (diagnosed as contact dermatitis) and lower back pain. Changing her diet and laundry detergent has not helped.

Reading: The rash is not caused by her diet, chemicals, or toxins but by her hormone level. (She then stated that the rash appeared after she had her hysterectomy.) Her hormones are very sensitive, and when she is tired or stressed her hormone level is affected. It is also 30% responsible for her weight gain. Acupuncture would help her.

F 55 yrs 03-26-01

Problem: She had a lump in her right breast a year ago that was negative for cancer on a mammogram. The lump is near her armpit, and it aches and burns at times. Her family has a history of cancer, and she is concerned about it. She also has had heart palpitations for 2 years. She wears an estrogen patch.

Reading: The lump is not cancerous, but it is hot and irritated. It comes and goes with her hormones, which kick off and on during the day. If she balances her hormones, the lump will calm down. The patch that she is wearing is not strong enough for later in the day when she becomes tired and stressed. The heart palpitations are both stress-and hormone-related. Her low hormone level is affecting her bones as well.

F 57 yrs 08-18-01

Problem: When she began menopause 4 years ago she also developed pin-prick pains at the back of her tongue that have since moved to the left ear, down the left breast, and into the left arm. The pain usually flares up once a month, and she has difficulty swallowing. MRIs, barium swallows, ECGs, and thyroid checks have been negative.

Reading: She is having an allergic reaction. Now that her hormones have changed and she no longer has menstrual cycles, her body is more sensitive to airborne pollens. Perhaps she could have a test of her female hormone levels and then try to raise her hormone levels—not because her body requires the increased level but so that she will stop reacting to the allergens. Traditional hormone replacement therapy probably would be more effective than acupuncture and herbs.

F 48 yrs 09-02-01

Problem: Sometimes when exercising her uterus feels as though it is about to fall out, but doctors cannot find anything wrong. This problem began when she started menopause.

Reading: Her uterine muscles are weak and are pulling on her bladder. Kegel exercises, acupuncture, and energy work to this area would be helpful.

M 70 yrs 10-14-01

Problem: His kidneys stopped functioning for 5 days 2 years ago, and he was given only hours to live. He is now very weak, his skin is dry and itchy, and he wakes up tired. Doctors do not know why his kidneys failed.

Reading: His kidneys are lacking vitamins and are the cause of his fatigue and weakness. He is also low in male hormones, which is the main cause of his dry skin and a contributing factor to his weakness. Perhaps his low hormone level also caused his kidney failure. His thymus gland needs stimulation to decrease his fatigue. Drinking apple cider vinegar would help his kidney function, and the potassium in the vinegar would help his skin and energy problems as well. He needs B vitamins in liquid form for his kidneys, as well as acupuncture.

INSECT/ANIMAL BITES

F 52 yrs 06-03-01

Problem: She had a tremor on her right side 12 years ago, and then she began to drag her foot. Today she is in a wheelchair. Although her upper body has sensation, she has none in her lower body and her muscles do not function at all. Doctors have ruled out ALS (Lou Gehrig's disease) and multiple sclerosis. MRIs and spinal taps have been negative. A tick bit her 13 years ago.

Reading: She was exposed to a chemical–possibly from the tick bite– that has affected her thyroid gland. Energy to the thyroid gland has been split 60% to one side and 40% to the other, and her thymus gland may have been affected as well. Both glands should be treated with acupuncture for 30 days, and her condition would improve.

F 39 yrs 06-09-01

Problem: Six years ago she began to feel very tired and could not stay awake. Her right index finger and both knees became painful, but cortisone injections helped. After 5 years of fatigue she was diagnosed with Lyme disease caused by a tick that may have been on her dog. A year ago she could not hold anything in her hands, be touched, go to the bathroom alone, or even brush her teeth. She was in a wheelchair for 6 months, but physical therapy enabled her to get around with canes. Now the body pain seems to cycle. For 2 days it is more severe in her upper body, and then 2 days later it is worse in the lower body. She stopped taking her pain medication because she believed that it was making her Lyme disease worse. She is stiff and weak, has patches of numbness, and has lumps on the tendons of her hands and the bottoms of her feet.

Reading: The Lyme disease diagnosis may be correct because it first affected her blood and then attacked the nervous system and the nerves in specific organs, particularly the kidneys. (She agreed that she has had multiple kidney infections since this happened.) The kidneys are the most important factor in the healing of the rest of her body. She needs high protein intake to help restore the nerves to her kidneys and other organs and vitamin B_{12} injections to help restore kidney function. Oral doses likely will not help. The spinal cord has been affected, but it appears to be 85% restored.

F 29 yrs 04-21-01

Problem: Her bladder, small intestine, uterus, and rectum were prolapsed. To repair them surgeons removed her left ovary and uterus. She now has had throbbing bladder pain for 3 years. Two years ago doctors diagnosed it as interstitial cystitis, a disease of the bladder lining. When urine enters the bladder, she has excruciating pain. She has to urinate 60 times a day. She is taking a medication that rebuilds the bladder lining. Acupuncture has not helped, and massage therapy helps the stress but not the bladder pain.

Reading: She may have been stung by an insect and the poison entered her spinal fluid, after which it entered the intestinal tract and then the bladder. (She agreed that she was bitten on the leg and it swelled up severely.) Acupuncture to her bladder would help her.

F 53 yrs 07-16-01
Problem: She was diagnosed with Parkinson's disease 3 years ago. Medication helps control her twitching, although stress tends to make it worse. At times she also has esophageal reflux. She wants to know what she can do to cope with these problems.
Reading: An animal bite–possibly from a rabid animal–caused a blood reaction in her body, which caused heavy metals in her blood to react to the infection. This reaction disrupted the nerves in her head, causing the twitching and parkinsonism, which in turn is causing the reflux. (She stated that a squirrel bit her when she was 9 years of age.) She needs acupuncture for her brain area and toxins removed from her blood. She also should eat according to her blood type and avoid foods that make her blood more toxic, such as those containing yeast and other fungi.

JOINT PROBLEMS

F 43 yrs 11-02-98
Problem: She has chronic joint pain. She is taking estrogen after having had a hysterectomy 6 years ago.
Reading: The joint pain is related to her high blood sugar levels, not the estrogen. She is also low in minerals.

M 50 yrs 06-19-00
Problem: He has stiffness in his hands, feet, and hips.
Reading: Eating according to his blood type should reduce the joint discomfort.

F 25 yrs 04-03-00

Problem: She has joint pain and has been told that her cartilage is the cause, not a disk.

Reading: The joint pain is caused by a problem with her cartilage. She was born with it. It is most likely a protein deficiency from one of her parents, perhaps linked to drug use. (She then related that her father had terminal cancer and used marijuana at the time that she was conceived.)

M 33 yrs 12-09-99

Problem: Both of his knees bother him, although he has not had them examined. He seems not to be absorbing his foods and cannot gain weight.

Reading: He is low in vitamins and minerals because of the poor dietary absorption, and this has contributed to some of the knee pain. His digestive enzymes are low, and he does not get enough good yeast, possibly because of having had valley fever (a virus) 5 years ago. He needs to drink more water and increase the good yeast.

F 42 yrs 07-26-98

Problem: She has a painful hip, weak hip muscles, and wrist pain. She has experienced a lot of stress over the past 5 years.

Reading: The hip needs an adjustment, and the hip ligaments are very tight. Her muscles are tired because of the joint pain. She needs to do stretching exercises. She also needs vitamin and mineral supplements, minerals more than vitamins, particularly potassium. The potassium would help her wrists as well. She carries a lot of her stress in the jaw joint and neck muscles. If she can learn to relax this area, her body will not tire as quickly. Her body needs to catch up with her mind. Her mind has improved in its healing, but her body has not moved at the same rate. Yoga and yogic breathing would help.

F 27 yrs 04-05-99

Problem: She has pain in her ankles, hands, knees, jaw, and neck. She was diagnosed with lupus, and her naturopathic doctor believes that she has too much mercury in her teeth.

Reading: She likely does not have lupus, although the naturopathic doctor is correct about the high mercury level in her bloodstream. It is causing the joint pain, and she is also high in other minerals such as copper and aluminum. Her liver is toxic, and the pancreas is exhausted. She needs help, such as hypnosis, in dealing with stress. Her brain is releasing (or overproducing) minerals, most likely a result of the pituitary gland being stressed and in need of restoration. She should have reflexology to treat the pituitary gland, pancreas, and liver.

F 39 yrs 11-01-98

Problem: She has joint pain.

Reading: She will have less joint pain when she eliminates salt from her diet. She craves salt and eats a lot of foods with sodium used as a preservative. She needs to eat more natural foods and avoid salt completely.

F 59 yrs 01-25-99

Problem: She has joint and general body stiffness.

Reading: She should eat according to her blood type and avoid breads especially. She needs breathing and stretching exercises. She is stiff because of a lack of exercise and poor diet. She might try exercises such as badminton and water aerobics.

F 32 yrs 03-29-99

Problem: She has joint pain, mainly in the knees, which began 3 years ago when her first child was born. She now has another child and the pain has gotten worse, extending into the bottoms of her feet and hands. She has been seeing a rheumatologist who has not found the cause. A podiatrist diagnosed flat feet for which she was given corrective shoes, but they have not helped either.

Reading: Her blood is toxic because of her liver and stomach, and maybe her gallbladder as well, but her stomach is the main factor. It has a high content of fatty buildup, and her liver is tired from working on the problem. This has affected her blood, which in turn has affected the joints. She also does not produce enough enzymes to dissolve her food. First she needs to see a naturopath for an herb that will cleanse the stomach and liver. Then she needs a product such as an enzyme that will help her dissolve her foods. She could start with apple cider vinegar.

M 39 yrs 09-13-99
Problem: He has knee discomfort. Doctors are concerned about his high liver enzyme level.
Reading: The liver problem is diet-related. He needs to eat according to his blood type and stop eating salt. He retains water, which is causing the pain in his knees. He should take herbs to treat his liver.

F 56 yrs 11-18-99
Problem: She has joint stiffness. As a child she had rheumatic fever, which can affect the joints and heart. She is on hormone replacement therapy. She is also having difficulty losing weight.
Reading: The joint pain will go away once she gets on a natural hormone, exercises (cardiovascular and weight training), and eats properly.

F 44 yrs 10-19-98
Problem: She has joint pain. She is concerned that the mercury fillings in her teeth are causing problems with her health.
Reading: The filling material could be draining into her bloodstream, causing the joint pain.

F 42 yrs 07-26-98
Problem: She has joint pain, muscle weakness, and fatigue after a workout. She wonders if exercise hurts or helps her.
Reading: The muscle weakness is related to her joint pain. She needs to do stretching exercises. She also needs vitamin and mineral supplements, minerals more than vitamins, particularly potassium.

M 46 yrs 08-28-00
Problem: His joints feel as though the tissues are weak or thin, especially in the knees.
Reading: He needs dietary oils to increase lubrication to the joint tissue. He also should eat according to his blood type, drink apple cider vinegar, and avoid alcohol and dark-colored carbonated soft drinks. He is not toxic—just dry.

F 41 yrs 07-12-01
Problem: She has hip, thoracic, sciatic, and joint pain. For the past 3 years her life has been very stressful.
Reading: She is deficient in vitamins A, D, C, and E (her B looks okay) and perhaps even a mineral that helps the body cope with joint pain. The stress in her life might have drained her body of these nutrients. Replacing these vitamins should eliminate the back, hip, and joint pain.

F 38 yrs 07-11-01
Problem: She has joint and muscle pain in her shoulders, neck, arms, elbows, and knees. She also has had high blood pressure for the past 3 months for which she is taking medication.
Reading: She lacks a mineral for joint cartilage—likely it is sulfur, but she needs a consultation about this. Her kidneys need sulfur to function better; this would prevent the joint and muscle aches and keep her blood pressure under control.

KIDNEY PROBLEMS

F 39 yrs 06-20-00
Problem: She has back pain. An MRI has revealed degenerated lumbar disks.

Reading: Her kidneys are weak and a factor in her back pain. She needs more water, cranberry juice, and plenty of other liquids. If she increases her fluids by 70%, she will have less back pain.

M 62 yrs 09-28-99

Problem: He is depressed, bipolar, and taking many strong medications, such as lithium, for these problems. In the last 3 weeks he has gained 20 pounds, mostly water weight, and cannot put his shoes on because of the fluid buildup in his legs.

Reading: His main physical problem is his kidneys, and they are the primary cause of his water retention. This is occurring because his medications are too strong. He needs to see a naturopathic physician for St. John's Wort and other herbs, which would enable him to wean off his strong antidepression medications. Acupuncture also would help with the depression.

M 54 yrs 11-26-99

Problem: He is taking medications for depression. He has low blood pressure, stomach ulcers, and body pain and has lost 10 pounds in 7 days.

Reading: He is depleted of minerals. His kidneys are failing because of the adrenal glands, which are depleted because of a lack of minerals. The medication that he is taking for depression is having a negative affect on his adrenal glands. He needs to be on a natural herb for his depression, and his urine should be tested to determine mineral loss.

F 59 yrs 07-24-00

Reading: She has had long-time kidney disease, and one kidney has been removed. She was told 3 months ago that she has hypoactive thyroid and adrenal glands. She also has difficulty sleeping and is frequently nauseated.

Reading: Her pituitary gland and the hormones governed by the pituitary gland are the two main issues. First she needs to stabilize the pituitary gland, and then she needs her hormones balanced. The sleeping disorder is hormone-related; it is not caused by her diet or stress.

She is prone to dehydration and must drink plenty of fluids to avoid more kidney problems. Her pituitary gland is the main factor in her kidney disease and the cause of the loss of her kidney.

F 49 yrs 06-29-99
Problem: She wants a general health reading.
Reading: Her kidneys and liver need flushing. She should drink plenty of cranberry juice and apple cider vinegar.

F 31 yrs 12-14-99
Problem: She has a history of kidney stones and has had two removed.
Reading: Her kidneys are borderline diseased, and she needs to take this condition very seriously. Diet will help her kidneys the most. She has a tendency to produce a chemical that forms stones. Her kidneys have a hard time filtering fats, and she should avoid them along with yeast and starch. She needs to see a nephrologist.

F 66 yrs 01-28-01
Problem: She has kidney problems and a herpesvirus infection.
Reading: A hormone imbalance stemming from the ovaries is causing a rush of hormones through the kidneys and affecting their performance. This may be causing the herpesvirus to stay active. The herpesvirus infection is not stress-related; it is physically caused. She should drink apple cider vinegar for the kidneys, and the virus likely will subside. Acupuncture for the kidneys would help as well.

F 62 yrs 06-30-01
Problem: She was diagnosed with a rare blood disorder in which the white blood cells (WBCs) build up, causing great fatigue. After about 2 weeks they are eliminated, and she feels well again. Doctors do not know what causes it or how to treat it. She also suffers from chronic headaches across the forehead and temples for which she takes aspirin. She can feel the tension pulling her head backward, making her neck sore.
Reading: Either the WBCs are causing a kidney and bladder malfunc-

tion or the kidneys are causing the blood disorder, but it is likely the latter. When blood to the kidneys does not flow normally, this affects the blood in her spine, which drains or reduces the blood flow to the head, causing the light headaches. The tension she is feeling in her forehead and neck is actually the lack of blood flow. She is feeling a draining of blood going back down the head and traveling down the spine. Her condition could be compared with holding a water hose upright and not having enough water pressure to force the water out through the top so it travels back down the hose. Acupuncture might fix the kidney and bladder problem, and this in turn could fix the WBC problem.

M 70 yrs 08-06-01

Problem: He developed a body itch 18 months ago that causes him to scratch so much that his skin bleeds. Topical lotions have not helped, although acupuncture did help somewhat. A test showing high blood protein suggests that he has kidney problems.

Reading: His kidneys are causing the itching because of a high uric acid content. He needs to flush his kidneys with liquids and take medications that would help counter the high levels of uric acid. Acupuncture would improve his kidney function 25% to 30%, but it will take medication to help him the most. If he does not improve his kidney condition, his bladder may become toxic, poisoned by his urine.

F 7 yrs 07-08-01

Problem: She was diagnosed with lupus 2 years ago. She has a lot of joint pain, her teeth are becoming loose, she has no energy, and she cannot walk. Children of this age rarely have lupus. Three specialists have seen her, but they have not been able to help. Her mother keeps her out of sunlight and feeds her vegetable juices, but she wants to know what else she can do to help her daughter.

Reading: Her kidneys are most likely the cause of the lupus. (Her mother then stated that her daughter has had chronic kidney and urinary problems since having been diagnosed with lupus.) Doctors should focus on treating the kidneys to control or reverse the lupus. Her blood cells are being altered when the blood passes through the kidneys. This altered blood then affects her bowels as well, and she must be regulated to eliminate toxins. This can be controlled by diet to promote at least one but preferably two bowel movements a day. The kidneys can be treated with acupuncture and vitamins, especially A and B, which would help her red blood cells. Diet would help as well. She should also eat according to her blood type.

M 70 yrs 10-14-01
Problem: His kidneys stopped functioning for 5 days 2 years ago, and he was given only hours to live. He is now very weak, his skin is dry and itchy, and he wakes up tired. Doctors do not know why his kidneys failed.
Reading: His kidneys are lacking vitamins and are the cause of his fatigue and weakness. He is also low in male hormones, which is the main cause of his dry skin and a contributing factor to his weakness. Perhaps his low hormone level also caused his kidney failure. His thymus gland needs stimulation to improve his fatigue. Drinking apple cider vinegar would help his kidney function, and the potassium in the vinegar would help his skin and energy problems. He needs B vitamins in liquid form for his kidneys, as well as acupuncture.

LEG DISCOMFORT

F 64 yrs 07-30-97
Problem: She has leg pain that starts below the knee and radiates upward. Disk problems have been ruled out.
Reading: She has either a very low groin strain or a low stomach muscle strain. The area is inflamed or irritated, and nerves in the groin

area are radiating down into the thigh. Because of this, she has shifted her weight off the leg and adjusted her walk, causing muscle or nerve irritation. This is why her leg hurts. (After the reading she confirmed that she had a groin strain 4 years earlier.)

F 45 yrs 01-31-99
Problem: She has fatigued leg muscles.
Reading: Her back is out of alignment, which prevents energy flow to the legs. Her lumbar and pelvic areas look jammed together. She needs soft tissue work such as Rolfing and a chiropractor for an adjustment. This combination will help eliminate the leg pain and muscle fatigue. She also needs potassium and iron.

F 75 yrs 11-27-00
Problem: She was diagnosed with circulatory problems as the cause of her calf pain.
Reading: Her organs all look good, as does her circulation. The pain in her calf is coming from arthritis in her lower lumbar region. The pain increases when she is sitting for too long.

LIVER PROBLEMS

M 30 yrs 07-08-00
Problem: He began losing his hair at 15 years of age.
Reading: His diet is an important factor in his hair loss. He needs B vitamins, and he should avoid fatty foods. His liver is toxic and contributes to the hair loss. Selenium would be good for his age spots and toxic liver, and he should drink apple cider vinegar.

M 39 yrs 09-13-99
Problem: He has a high liver enzyme level.
Reading: His liver problem is diet-related. He needs to eat according to his blood type and see a naturopath for herbs that would help his liver.

F 49 yrs 06-29-99
Problem: This is a follow-up to a previous reading.
Reading: Her kidneys and liver need flushing. She should drink plenty of cranberry juice and apple cider vinegar.

F 72 yrs 08-02-97
Problem: She has stomach and gastric problems; upper and lower gastrointestinal tests were negative.
Reading: Her problem in the upper diaphragm area could be liver-related. Her liver is toxic. This could be a nerve problem caused by a vertebra in her back. She should see a naturopathic doctor for cleansing the liver and a chiropractor for the problem with the vertebra.

F 27 yrs 05-08-00
Problem: She has had irregular menstrual periods for 13 years. For the past 3 years she has had a warm and itchy skin rash that resembles hives.
Reading: Both the liver and pancreas are toxic and are linked to the irregular periods and skin rash. Fried foods are the cause. She needs to flush both organs with herbs and see a naturopath accordingly.

F 45 yrs 12-03-97
Problem: She is concerned about her liver. Lately she has not been feeling well, and her family has a history of liver problems.
Reading: Her liver is functioning, but it is very sluggish. She needs to be very careful putting demands on it for this reason. She should drink plenty of water and see a naturopath for an herb that can help flush her liver.

F 59 yrs 01-29-01

Problem: She requires a liver transplant. She is losing muscle mass and wants to know what is causing her problem. Doctors want her to take steroids, but she refuses. She was a heavy alcohol drinker for 20 years.
Reading: Her liver is enlarged and appears to have been exposed to poison. (She then stated that years earlier she had drunk gasoline by mistake.) The problem is also lung-related. She has too much oxygen to the liver but not enough blood flow for adequate filtration. This is causing the liver to be enlarged. The lungs are enlarged as well. She needs to increase blood flow but reduce oxygen in the liver to remove the toxins. One side of her chest has an energy blockage. Energy work to the lungs and liver, along with acupuncture and reflexology, would help her.

F 48 yrs 02-03-01

Problem: She was diagnosed with hepatitis C.
Reading: The hepatitis C has affected both her liver and aorta. Her brain is sluggish because of the hepatitis. She needs to take an herb that would increase oxygen to the brain and lie on a recline board (head lower than the feet) for 10 minutes at the end of the day to promote blood flow to her brain.

M 60 yrs 02-10-01

Problem: He has psoriasis and is worried that he might have skin cancer. He has back and joint pain as well.
Reading: His liver is toxic, causing the age spots and psoriasis. The back and joint pain are not a structural problem; they are a result of toxic blood that stems from the liver. He should drink apple cider vinegar to detoxify his liver. He does not have skin cancer, but he does need to work on his liver.

F 70 yrs 03-01-01

Problem: She has been ill most of her life and seen by one doctor after another for many years. For the past 5years she has had numbness in her right leg and foot, inability to walk, loss of speech, tremors, and

THE WAY I SEE IT 199

body pain. She has lost the enamel from her teeth and is unable to eat carbohydrates. MRIs and other tests have been negative.

Reading: Bile and toxins are abundant in her blood because of her liver, which began to shut down when she was in her teens and very frightened by something. (She then said that she had a very mean mother who tied her to her bed and beat her. She wet her bed until the time she was married. Her son died of choking 9 years ago.) Her emotional state caused the liver to shut down. Acupuncture and reflexology to the liver and herbs to flush it would help her. She also needs to see a psychotherapist.

F 74 yrs 02-16-01

Problem: She has been losing her hair for 40 years and has been diagnosed with alopecia, although she still has her eyebrows and eyelashes. Doctors do not know the cause. Her skin is sensitive to ultraviolet rays. She has had life-long stress and is being treated for "social anxiety."

Reading: Her red blood cell (RBC) count is low and is the cause of her alopecia. This blood cell problem is caused by her liver. Reflexology or acupuncture to the liver likely would raise her RBC count. Stress has caused the liver problem, and acupuncture treatments for stress may help as well. She should see a psychotherapist to help her deal with events that occurred during the early years of her life. She is further along in her treatment of her social anxieties than she might think.

M 55 yrs 02-11-01

Problem: He has had high blood pressure for 20 years for which he has been on medications, chelation therapy, and meditation, but nothing has been able to control it. Currently he is having sinus problems.

Reading: His heart and aorta look fine, but his liver looks toxic and is slightly enlarged. He needs energy work to the liver, including acupuncture and reflexology. He also should have a liver flush and watch his fat intake. Apple cider vinegar would be good for his liver. His sinus condition is connected to his liver problem.

14317-CALI

F 69 yrs 02-26-01
Problem: She had a stroke last year that affected her right shoulder, hand, and arm. She is currently on blood thinner and blood pressure medications.
Reading: She has a liver problem that eventually lead to her stroke. She needs to have her liver tested and to take herbs for a liver flush. Walking and swinging her arms, cycling, and light weight lifting will all help her overcome the effects of the stroke.

M 61 yrs 03-26-01
Problem: He has had high blood pressure for 25 years and wants to know what is causing it.
Reading: His liver is causing his high blood pressure, probably as a result of his alcohol consumption 25 years ago. Acupuncture and an herbal flush to the liver would help his condition. Eating according to his blood type would be very beneficial.

LUNG/RESPIRATORY PROBLEMS

F 66 yrs 03-19-98
Problem: She has lung congestion, difficulty breathing, and recent pneumonia.
Reading: The lung problem might be nerve-related. She should have a chiropractor or osteopath examine the vertebra in the back where the nerve that controls breathing is located.

F 46 yrs 05-08-00
Problem: She is frequently tired and is concerned about age spots.
Reading: She is tired because of a lack of oxygen to the brain. Her age spots are caused by dry skin and the lack of lung capacity. The lower portion of her lungs looks 30% congested, probably from allergies, with cigarettes as a secondary cause. She should take saunas, perform breathing exercises, and sleep with a small pillow or towel rolled up under her neck. She is also slightly low in minerals and could take potassium. A massage therapist might work on the shoulders and neck area.

F 45 yrs 01-31-99
Problem: She has difficulty breathing deeply.
Reading: This is brought on by allergies (pollen), polluted air, and anxiety. She needs to use a room air purifier when experiencing shortness of breath.

F 46 yrs 12-11-96
Problem: She has difficulty breathing.
Reading: Her heart needs oxygen. Because she is overweight, the weight is pressing on her diaphragm, making it difficult for her to breathe.

M 20 yrs 02-09-97
Problem: He has chest congestion.
Reading: His lungs are too congested for a 20 year old, and his smoking is a contributing factor. He is not athletic, and his congestion would clear or improve with aerobic exercise. His lungs are not strong, and they have little expansion when used. He has poor posture and needs to stand up straight. His overall health is okay, but it will not continue if he does not make changes.

F 59 yrs 04-10-98
Problem: She has frequent bronchitis.
Reading: Her bronchitis is animal-related. She is allergic to pets, dogs in particular. A room air purifier will help her more than anything else.

F 53 yrs 05-08-00
Problem: She has had shortness of breath for 2 years and a cough for 1 year.
Reading: The shortness of breath is caused by her emotions. The cough is 40% caused by dry air and 60% caused by her emotions.

M 47 yrs 04-19-00
Problem: He asked for a general health reading.
Reading: His bronchial tubes are irritated, although his lungs are okay. He has only about a 55% oxygen level in his blood. He needs to quit smoking because it is affecting his bronchial tubes and depleting the oxygen in his blood.

F 62 yrs 02-27-01
Problem: She has had breathing problems ever since she moved to the high altitude of New Mexico. Doctors have tested her, but they cannot find anything wrong. She has panic attacks when she cannot breathe. She had the same problem when she was very young, but it went away.
Reading: Her problem is with chocolate. (She said that she loves chocolate and eats it at least twice a week.) When she eats chocolate the nerves in her throat contract the muscles in her upper throat, which cuts off the air supply, and this causes her to panic. Her thyroid gland is the main cause of her chocolate craving, and her adrenal gland is the secondary cause.

F 35 yrs 07-15-01
Problem: She was diagnosed with diffuse interstitial lung fibrosis 5 years ago. Her lungs are stiff and do not expand properly when she breathes. This condition is expected to worsen as she ages and could result in her death. She also has migraine headaches, dizziness, narcolepsy, and seizure-type symptoms. Doctors do not know what caused this disease, although birds and chemicals are commonly implicated.
Reading: A parasite is the cause of all of her symptoms. Eliminating the parasite should improve all of her symptoms except the lung problem.

For the lungs she needs deep upper shoulder and back massage with herbal oils. This oil should be left on the body for optimal absorption. This massage, along with acupuncture to the lungs, should help the fibrosis.

M 44 yrs 04-15-01
Problem: He has acne and clogged pores. He is also losing his hair, and his body temperature is lower than normal. Doctors at first believed that he had a hypothyroid condition, but tests have shown his thyroid to be normal.
Reading: His blood looks a little thick and shows high levels of nicotine, alcohol, and caffeine. He is not a smoker, but he is in a room full of smoke every day. (He states that he is a welder and is around exhaust all day long.) He is breathing these gases into his lungs, which is affecting his blood and the pores in his head. This is an environmental problem, and it is also causing the hair loss. He needs to wear a hat and a better facemask when he is working around cars, get more sunlight for his head, drink pure water, and breathe pure air. He also needs to perform breathing exercises. His lungs are clogged and dirty and need to be cleansed. His lungs are the cause of his low body temperature as well.

LUPUS

F 27 yrs 04-05-99
Problem: She was diagnosed with lupus 2 years ago. Her naturopathic doctor believes that she has too much mercury in her teeth. Recently she has been losing a lot of hair. She has pain in her ankles, hands,

knees, jaw, and neck. She has been diagnosed with leaky gut syndrome as well.

Reading: She likely does not have lupus. The naturopathic doctor is correct about the high mercury level in her bloodstream. It is causing the joint pain, but she also has a high level of other minerals such as copper and aluminum. Her liver is toxic, and her pituitary gland is exhausted. The leaky gut will not get completely better until they have been restored. She needs help in dealing with stress, such as hypnosis. Her brain is releasing (or overproducing) minerals, most likely a result of the pituitary gland being stressed and in need of restoration. She needs reflexology to treat the pituitary gland, pancreas, and liver. The hair loss is linked to the problems with her pituitary gland.

F 27 yrs 04-02-98

Problem: She was diagnosed with lupus 5 months ago and is being treated with an antimalaria drug, which has suppressed the disease symptoms.

Reading: The thymus gland needs to be stimulated. Her gallbladder, spleen, liver, and maybe her stomach should be checked for parasites. She needs to see a practitioner such as a naturopathic doctor to flush these organs. They are not functioning properly, either because of a parasite or blood disorder. The blood looks toxic and lacks oxygen, and the blood cells look infected. This is in an advanced stage but not yet to the point where it cannot be helped. She needs to get in touch with her body and breathe consciously. She should work her mind and body together and improve her diet as well. Spiritually she is very low and needs to get more connected with God. The blood disorder should be treated first, followed by work on a minor energy blockage. The antimalaria drug is very toxic to her organs and is having a negative influence on her. Her emotions are a major factor in her physical health. She needs to care about herself more.

M 41 yrs 05-02-01

Problem: He was diagnosed with lupus, for which he is taking prednisone. He wants to stop taking the medication because he does not believe that he has this disease. When he was a teenager he had a brain hemorrhage and was in a coma for 10 days. He had severe bruising all over his body, and doctors diagnosed his condition as idiopathic thrombocytopenia purpura, which entails not having enough platelets to clot the blood. His spleen was removed at that time.

Reading: Energy appears to be flat on the top of his head and unable to leave through the crown. As a result his brain seems to be pressing down on his glands and fluids. This blocked energy has been there for most of his life, most likely caused by a viral infection. He is ill because the blockage is putting pressure on the fluids in his brain. He needs acupuncture or other energy work to the top of his head.

F 7 yrs 07-08-01

Problem: She was diagnosed with lupus 2 years ago. She has a lot of joint pain, her teeth are becoming loose, she has no energy, and she cannot walk. Children of this age rarely have lupus. Three specialists have seen her, but they have been of little help. Her mother keeps her out of the sunlight and feeds her vegetable juices, but she wants to know what else she can do to help her daughter.

Reading: Her kidneys are most likely the cause of the lupus. (Her mother then stated that her daughter has had chronic kidney and urinary problems since having been diagnosed with lupus.) Doctors should focus on treating the kidneys to control or reverse the lupus. Her blood cells are being altered when the blood passes through the kidneys. his altered blood then affects the bowels as well, and she must be her regulated to eliminate toxins. This can be controlled by diet to promote at least one but preferably two bowel movements a day. The kidneys can be treated with acupuncture and vitamins, especially A and B, which would help her red blood cells. Diet would help as well, and she should also eat according to her blood type.

F 64 yrs 08-08-01

Problem: She was diagnosed with lupus. Symptoms include left-sided weakness, vomiting, diarrhea, confusion, dizziness, shakiness, and fatigue. She also has high blood pressure and recently has begun falling at night.

Reading: A chemical released from the middle brain is affecting her nervous system, particularly a nerve in the lower back, and this elicits the shakiness and loss of muscle strength that causes her to fall. This chemical is quickly absorbed, and her strength returns to her leg muscles in a few minutes. Her immune system cannot handle this chemical in her current state (lupus), which is why it is having such a negative effect on her nervous system. She should see a specialist who could identify this chemical and control its release from her brain, if possible, so that this process can be stopped or reduced. Her lupus is connected to her liver. She needs her liver treated with acupuncture and detoxified via a very strict vegetarian diet. This will improve the lupus symptoms, vomiting, and diarrhea.

LYMPHATIC PROBLEMS

F 39 yrs 02-21-00

Problem: She has had headaches for the last 7 months and ear pain and strep throat for the past year.

Reading: She has a lymphatic disorder in the base of the neck near the clavicle for which she needs to be treated. First she eats foods that form toxins, and then the blocked lymph node prevents the toxins from moving out of the body and the brain, causing the headaches. She needs to eat according to her blood type. This will decrease the toxins and improve the headaches within 3 months. Her ear and throat problems are related to the lymphatic disorder as well.

F 42 yrs 01-16-00
Problem: She wants her lymphatic channels examined.
Reading: She has mild lymphatic blockage throughout her body. Lymphatic massage would help improve this condition.

M 44 yrs 01-08-01
Problem: He has chronic fatigue. He was first diagnosed 15 years ago and suffered a relapse 6 months ago. At that time he was given an injection in his left arm for the chronic fatigue and ever since then he has experienced severe pain in that arm and chest. He has also been having frequent colds.
Reading: The soft tissue in his neck and throat–most likely lymphatic–has been affected; this is the reason for his health problems and the cause of the chronic fatigue syndrome. He has an energy blockage in the neck that needs to be released, and this will help the lymphatic system drain properly. He holds stress in neck as well. The sides of his brain are also a concern because the fatigue syndrome has affected these areas. The virus is dormant in the body and activated at times by the energy block to the lymphatic tissue in the neck.

F 52 yrs 06-02-01
Problem: She has had ringing in her ears for the past 3 years. She also has high cholesterol and is under a lot of family stress.
Reading: The ringing in her ears is caused by pressure in the vein that runs along the side of her neck. Her lymphatic system is getting clogged and needs to be treated. She should have lymphatic massage or reflexology to the lymphatic system in the chest and armpits to promote drainage. She also needs to reduce her cholesterol so that the neck vein does not get worse. Her adrenal glands are 50% depleted as a result of stress and are raising her cholesterol levels.

MEMORY PROBLEMS, CONCENTRATION

F 64 yrs 04-03-00
Problem: She is concerned about her memory and overall energy; she was diagnosed with chronic fatigue syndrome.
Reading: Her mind needs exercise and memory work. Her memory problems are connected to the chronic fatigue, which is linked to her heart. Her heart looks sluggish and needs exercise. The fatigue also could be linked to her hormone level, which should be tested by a doctor.

F 52 yrs 12-13-98
Problem: She has memory loss problems; she is concerned that she does not think as clearly as she used to.
Reading: Her memory loss would improve with potassium, which she could get from drinking apple cider vinegar. She is also emotionally exhausted and needs more physical rest.

F 68 yrs 12-10-99
Problem: She is concerned about her memory, short-term more than long-term.
Reading: She has severe mineral deficiency, particularly of zinc and potassium.

M 40 yrs 01-24-99
Problem: He has had poor memory for the past 2 years; he gets confused when trying to make a decision.

Reading: His memory loss and confusion are diet-and stress-related. Nothing is wrong with his mind. He should avoid sugar, chocolate, and caffeine.

F 46 yrs 11-23-98

Problem: Her memory is not as sharp as it used to be. She has difficulty learning new things, and she forgets things that she believes are important.

Reading: Her memory problem is a combination of two things: a lack of oxygen and a nerve that runs from the crown of the head on the left side down along the back of the head. The nerve problem could be helped with reflexology. Exercising the cardiovascular system would increase oxygen and help stimulate her brain. Her lungs are clear, but they are sluggish and lack oxygen.

F 66 yrs 10-05-99

Problem: She is concerned about memory loss.

Reading: The memory loss is a valid concern. She needs to take mineral supplements.

F 49 yrs 03-24-00

Problem: She is concerned about memory loss; she also lacks energy and does not sleep well.

Reading: Her memory loss problem is related primarily to a mineral deficiency caused by poor diet and stress. Her sleeping problem and low energy also affect her memory.

F 43 yrs 02-21-99

Problem: She has a lack of mental focus. She is accustomed to focusing at a higher level.

Reading: The lack of focus is mineral-related. She needs zinc, potassium, and other minerals in general. She sleeps 5 to 6 hours per night. Raising the mineral levels will also help her sleep longer, which will help her concentration.

F 68 yrs 01-06-01
Problem: She would like to have her brain looked at because she is having memory problems.
Reading: Her energy is blocked from the front to the back of her head, and it is age-related. She needs energy work to prevent memory loss. She should also perform memory exercises.

MENSTRUAL CYCLE ISSUES

F 32 yrs 04-16-98
Problem: She had a recent hospitalization for uncontrolled menstrual bleeding. Doctors do not know the cause, nor are they able to stop it.
Reading: The bleeding is related to her emotional state. She also eats too much sugar to control her emotions. When she was very young she likely was yelled at or witnessed this yelling and it scared her. Because of this she reacts strongly to being yelled at. She also wakes up between 1 and 3 AM every morning and believes that a liver disorder is causing the interrupted sleep; however, it is emotional. She was adopted and tends to need compassion and attention, particularly during her menstrual cycles. However, her parents cannot sense this need, and in fact they shelter her too much as it is. She could use positive hypnosis tapes, particularly at night while trying to sleep and a week before her monthly periods.

F 24 yrs 10-18-99
Problem: She has irregular menstrual periods. One year they are regular, and the next they are absent. This has been going on since she was 14 years of age. She has two children.
Reading: Her ovaries are healthy but inactive. She likely suffered some

form of mental trauma as a child, and this is the main cause of her irregular periods. She has not dealt with this trauma and has shut down emotionally. Most of her physical problems are emotionally based. Her emotional state needs treatment, and her ovaries would benefit from energy work.

F 39 yrs 02-21-00
Problem: She has had heavy menstrual bleeding for the past year.
Reading: Her heavy bleeding is linked to her hormones, which are produced as a reaction to her diet. She needs to eat according to her blood type. She may need hormone supplements if she changes her diet.

F 27 yrs 05-08-00
Problem: She has irregular menstrual periods. She wonders if she is capable of becoming pregnant.
Reading: Both her liver and pancreas are toxic and linked to the irregular periods. Fried foods are the cause. She needs to see a naturopath and have both organs flushed with herbs. She can become pregnant, but her emotional side will slow this down. She is very concerned about her personal life.

F 31 yrs 06-02-00
Problem: She has had irregular menstrual periods for the past 4 to 5 months.
Reading: Her hormones are okay, but the pituitary gland needs to be checked. Her stress level affects her pituitary gland.

F 29 yrs 01-07-01
Problem: She bleeds a lot and feels very weak during her menstrual periods.
Reading: Overall she is low in vitamins (though not in minerals). Before her periods she should take vitamin B_{12}, perhaps even by injection. This problem is emotionally driven.

F 42 yrs 06-18-01

Problem: Two years ago she began having symptoms of fatigue so great that her arms felt like rubber. She was also light-headed and weak with a sensation of pressure in her head. Doctors suggested that she may have an allergy problem, but she disagrees. Her symptoms are severe one day and slight the next.

Reading: The problem is most likely her reproductive hormones kicking off and on, releasing hormones irregularly into her body. (She said that 6 months earlier she had had a D&C and now her menstrual periods are back to normal.) She will probably experience heavy bleeding and weakness again within the next year or so, but then she will enter menopause and her periods, fatigue, and weakness will go away. For now she should have her hormone levels checked.

MENTAL RETARDATION

M 28 yrs 06-14-01

Problem: After he was born he was slow to develop, walk, and talk. He was happy but hyperactive. By 4 years of age he was still not potty trained. At 10 years of age he was sent to a group home because his parents could not control him due to his hyperactivity. Then he went from foster home to foster home and is now at an assistance center, where he is locked up in a room by himself because he strikes out at staff members and defecates on the floor and walls. His diagnosis is mental retardation, and his parents are desperate to know what to do for him. He is currently being treated with electric shock therapy.

Reading: Electric shock therapy will not help him because he does not have a nerve disorder. He has an underdeveloped brain. At birth his brain and connected nervous system were lacking the necessary vitamins, such as A, D, and E, and therefore were not properly developed. He should be treated nutritionally with vitamin injections, even into the spinal fluid and brainstem if possible so that the vitamins can reach the bloodstream in the brain. He also needs protein injections and maybe even low-level growth hormone injections to help develop his brain. Optimally his parents should bring in a nutritionist to help their son. (The mother stated that when their son was born, the doctor told them to give him vitamins to help him develop but they could not afford them at the time.)

M 12 yrs 08-01-01

Problem: He was diagnosed with mild to moderate mental retardation. His mother believes that he is more in the autism category. He cannot read or write, and he cannot or will not speak. When he was 4 years of age, an MRI was normal.

Reading: His brain and body development appears to be normal, but he has very little energy running through his body and because of this he is not well grounded. This was present at birth. (His mother then stated that he was 2 months premature.) He needs energy work, acupuncture, and reflexology to stimulate his energy starting at the top of his head to the bottoms of his feet. First he needs his energy flow opened from head to toe, and then that energy needs to be brought together. This will help him become more connected and grounded and instill in him the desire to try harder. He appears capable of doing more than he does. His parents should try exercising his brain with simple card games and picture cards with words.

MERCURY/METALS EXPOSURE

M 33 yrs 12-09-99
Problem: He is concerned that the mercury fillings in his teeth are causing some of his health problems.
Reading: The mercury fillings are not a current issue but might be in the next 4 years.

F 27 yrs 04-05-99
Problem: She has pain in her ankles, hands, knees, jaw, and neck. Her naturopathic doctor believes that she has too much mercury in her teeth.
Reading: The naturopathic doctor is right about the high mercury level in her blood stream. It is causing the joint pain.

F 44 yrs 10-19-98
Problem: She had joint pain and is concerned that the mercury fillings in her teeth could be causing it.
Reading: The filling material could be draining into her bloodstream, causing the joint pain.

M 63 yrs 08-23-01
Problem: He was diagnosed 5 months ago with ALS, or Lou Gehrig's disease. Last year he had twitching in his arms that moved to his stomach and legs. He now lacks control over the muscles of his hands and legs and has trouble with speech and swallowing. He gets around with a walker and is taking an experimental medication. His thyroid gland

has tested both hyperactive and hypoactive, and an MRI has shown evidence of some spinal fluid leakage. His career once involved making lead bullets, and tests have shown that he has metal poisoning.

Reading: His ALS was most likely caused by his frequent exposure to the lead. His spleen and liver appear dark and toxic, most likely caused by lead exposure, and the poisoned blood from these organs is causing the twitching throughout his body and affecting his nervous system. His thyroid gland has been damaged by the lead, and the upper lobe is affecting his swallowing and speech. The leaking spinal fluid is also caused by the lead exposure and is an important factor in his strength or weakness. Acupuncture to the areas mentioned might help, but detoxifying the blood in his liver and spleen would bring the best results and might even improve his spinal cord. His symptoms should improve greatly once the lead is eliminated from his blood.

F 60 yrs 02-16-01

Problem: She was recently diagnosed with a progressive form of MS. Seven years earlier she awoke with a pain in her back, and symptoms have progressed since then.

Reading: She likely had a metal or mercury overdose or exposure that went into the bloodstream and is now manifesting in the mid-brain. (She then stated that she played with mercury as a child, had mercury fillings until 8 years ago, and also had anti-aging injections in Mexico, which probably contained metals.)

F 57 yrs 02-20-01

Problem: She has wheat intolerance, among other food sensitivities. Diagnostic tests have shown that she has high, toxic levels of metals in her system.

Reading: The back, upper portion of her brain has been exposed to chemicals, most likely oil-based chemicals and lead. (She then stated that she is an artist.) These likely are the metals showing up as toxic levels in her system. The wheat intolerance is a result of this chemical exposure. She should see a naturopathic physician for herbs that would cleanse her system of these metals.

MULTIPLE SCLEROSIS

F 38 yrs 12-15-99
Problem: She had a toothache 3 weeks ago. The dentist treated her, and when the pain returned she was told that nothing was wrong. Two years ago her ear swelled to twice its size. After taking antibiotics she was treated with acupuncture, which helped the pain temporarily, but then the pain returned. Doctors think that she has symptoms of multiple sclerosis (MS). She is on an antiepilepsy medication, which has helped the pain. She wants to know if her body is fighting cancer.
Reading: She does not have cancer or MS. A germ or bacteria in the blood has settled in her jaw. She likely had an open sore and the bacteria entered her mouth at that time. (She then explained that she has gum recession at the canine teeth, and this is where the pain has been). This was the site in which the bacteria entered the bloodstream.

F 43 yrs 04-17-96
Problem: She was diagnosed with MS. She had an accident 12 years ago and has pain, vision and digestive problems, and skin irritation at the shoulder blade area.
Reading: Her MS was caused mostly by the trauma from 12 years ago. The back of her head in the center of the skull has nerve involvement and needs to be the main focus of the healing. This nerve flares out across the center of the skull, affecting the cervical vertebrae and the lumbar and thoracic disks. The skull injury is the underlying cause of the neck, lower back, kidney, and lung problems. The skin irritation is nerve-related as well. She should attempt to exercise whenever she is mentally ready because this will help her heal physically, but she should

stop whenever she physically cannot continue. She is healing mentally quicker than she is physically, and this is frustrating to her, but she needs to be patient. Physical healing will most likely be long term–about 3 years. If she begins treatment now, she will feel better, but she will see considerable improvement in the third year.

F 46 yrs 04-25-98

Problem: She was diagnosed with MS 2 years ago. She has had a spot of severe pain at the upper left side of her neck near the spinal column for the past year that comes and goes. She believes it is emotionally based. The left side of her body feels very heavy and weak. She experiences pressure in the back left side of her head and numbness in her face. She also has pain in her intestines, which feels like a knot on the left side, and tingling in her left little toe. She wants to know if she can heal or how to deal with the MS.

Reading: The pain in her neck near the spine is physical and caused by the illness; however, the level of pain is controlled by her emotions. Her body is beginning to feel the stress to the spine and the ligaments and muscles around it. Controlling the stress will help relax the muscles and ligaments and take the strain off the vertebrae. Most of the pressure in the back of her head and facial numbness are a result of the MS. Massage therapy, hypnosis, and 30 minutes to 1 hour a day of total mind and body relaxation would help control the MS and minimize the pain, particularly in the area of the head. She has a large, dark circle in the back of and particularly to the side of the head that looks like energy blockage. Energy is very active within this circle, but it is blocked and cannot go beyond this circle and circulate within the entire brain. Energy work on the head–moving energy around and through the entire brain–will reduce or eliminate the head pain.

The pain in her intestinal tract is nerve-and muscle-related. Tingling in the little toe may be coming from the lower back, caused by nerve interference, and it is not a large concern. Both can be healed emotionally and physically, but emotionally more than physically. She has not wanted to heal and must start now before her body regresses further. To deal with the MS she needs to make a larger effort in the treatments just mentioned. She also needs to understand that her MS is at a very early stage and she can do a lot physically and emotionally so that it does not get worse. The type of MS that she has is fortunate because she can almost control it. However, this type of MS is going to get the best of her if she lets it. She has the ability to minimize its potential or threat. She needs to make this an exciting challenge and get those close to her involved as well.

F 54 yrs 08-20-00
Problem: She wonders if she has MS. She had a benign tumor on her thyroid gland removed and has nerve damage as a result.
Reading: The thyroid tumor developed as a reaction to radiation exposure. Although most of her thyroid was removed, the remaining gland could still form more benign lumps. The remaining gland and the thymus gland need stimulation through reflexology. The backside of the pituitary gland is slightly enlarged. This is a reaction to a nerve disorder perhaps caused by medication that she was given when she had the surgery. She does not have MS, but she does have a mild nerve disease that is most likely not going to get worse nor ever be identified. She also needs acupuncture for the pituitary and thyroid glands and homeopathic remedies for all the involved glands.

F 51 yrs 02-05-01
Problem: She fell from a three-story ladder 4 years ago. For the past 3 years she has been unable to move her arms and legs and is in a wheelchair. If she is lying down, her arms and legs relax, but if she is moved, her extremities tighten up. Four years ago a doctor diagnosed her as having MS, although two others have said that she does not have MS.
Reading: Two veins in her neck were stretched and sustained microtears when she fell. Her paralysis began at that time. This is not MS or a nerve injury but rather a lack of blood and oxygen supply to the extremities, which prevents them from functioning normally. She should see a physician who also performs acupuncture and consult a physical therapist for exercises to the front part of the neck.

F 17 yrs 07-19-01

Problem: She has had a muscle weakness problem since she was 15 months of age. She had difficulty sitting up and was slow to walk. Her knees pop out of their sockets and she may unexpectedly have a sharp muscle pain that runs down her arms, hands, and legs. This intense pain can last between 30 seconds and 3 minutes. Her muscles twitch under her eyes and in her fingers, upper arms, and thighs. One week these symptoms can occur several times and the next week not at all. Her voice also has a fast, low pitch. One MRI has shown white lesions on her brain, but a second showed none. Doctors are stumped and have tentatively diagnosed her as having MS.

Reading: Thousands of white crystals form on her brain (or pass over the top of her brain) and seep into her body, disrupting the natural flow of her nervous system. These crystals have the appearance of rain falling gently, covering and then saturating her muscles before being absorbed by the cells. This is why one MRI found them and the second did not.

She was born with abnormal adrenal glands, with one barely developed and the other of a more normal size. This adrenal dysfunction is causing this unusual chemical release. She needs to see an endocrinologist. If her adrenal glands are not diseased and are in fact developed sufficiently, this problem may be treatable.

F 54 yrs 02-14-01

Problem: She was diagnosed with MS based on clinical symptoms rather than laboratory work. Within 3 years of this diagnosis she was no longer able to walk.

Reading: She has a dark and hollow look to the front brain and sinus area. It looks as though she was exposed to a medication 20 years ago. (She then concurred that when she was in her early twenties she used LSD approximately 20 times.) She would benefit from acupuncture to the area of the brain that affects mood, speech, and motor function.

F 60 yrs 02-16-01

Problem: She was recently diagnosed with a progressive form of MS.

Seven years earlier she awoke with a pain in her back, and symptoms have progressed since then.

Reading: She likely had a metal or mercury overdose or exposure that went into the bloodstream and is now manifesting in the mid-brain. (She then stated that she played with mercury as a child, had mercury fillings until 8 years ago, and also had anti-aging injections in Mexico, which probably contained metals.)

M 71 yrs 03-03-01

Problem: Symptoms began with a pain in his left eye 20 years ago. Over the years symptoms have progressed to his entire left side. Today he is unable to move his left foot forward. He has had at least 25 medical opinions, 2 of which are that he has MS. He has had 15 spinal taps and MRIs and is now taking injections at $1000 per injection for MS.

Reading: Most likely he does not have MS. He has a blood vessel in his brain, possibly an aneurysm, that becomes swollen when his heart pumps and is putting pressure on the part of his brain that controls motor functioning. He should see a neurologist or neurosurgeon who can identify and reduce the pressure in the blood vessel and thereby improve his motor functioning.

MUSCLE PROBLEMS

F 39 yrs 07-19-98

Problem: She has reflex sympathetic dystrophy, a nerve disease. She has uncontrollable pain and muscle spasms and cannot bear anything touching her leg.

Reading: Drinking apple cider vinegar may help control the muscle spasms.

F 51 yrs 10-19-98

Problem: She has had neck, back, and shoulder pain for 9 years. She also has headaches and pain in her hip and down both legs.

Reading: She has severe muscle spasms in her neck, mid-back, and lower back. The main area of spasm is the upper middle back between the shoulders. The vertebra will not stay in place until the spasms are corrected. A chiropractor needs to focus first on this area. Once this area is fixed, the neck and lower back will respond better to treatment. The vertebrae in the neck that need adjustment have caused the neck spasms and are the main reason for the headaches and lack of sleep. The lower back is twisted and in spasm at the lower lumbar and pelvic areas.

F 42 yrs 09-24-99

Problem: Her health has been deteriorating for the past year. Last week she was hospitalized for abdominal pain that radiates to the right rib area and stabbing pains to her back. She also has low blood sugar and was told that she has blood in her urine.

Reading: The portal vein just to the inside of the gallbladder is in spasm. Pain medication will not help; she needs muscle relaxants for 4 to 5 days and a short-term antidepressant. Her low blood sugar is and has been a factor with this spasm. Symptoms did not show up until the stress kicked in. She is tight and stressed when going to bed and wakes up this way. She needs yoga, and she should avoid alcohol for a while. This spasm is putting pressure on the right kidney, slightly bruising it, which is why blood showed up in the urine.

F 49 yrs 09-04-00

Problem: She has intense muscle burning and soreness. She began weight training a year ago, at which time her muscles began getting sore. The soreness became more intense and lasted longer as time went on. Eventually she could not even go for walks. Her muscles feel as though they are burning, particularly from the waist down. She cannot sleep because of this muscle problem.

Reading: The main cause of her burning muscles is her adrenal glands. Her body seems to be producing or releasing too much alkali or acid into the muscle and tissue. The tissue and muscle give the appearance of being separated from each other–not torn or tearing–just not working in conjunction. An endocrinologist should look at the corticosteroid and androgen levels produced by her adrenal glands. This adrenal problem developed as a reaction to stress, which she must learn to control. She could see a naturopath about adrenal supplements. If she were to have adrenal acupuncture she would see improvement in 2 weeks with more improvement in 2 months.

F 17 yrs 07-19-01

Problem: She has had a muscle weakness problem since she was 15 months old. She had difficulty sitting up and was slow to walk. Her knees pop out of their sockets, and she may unexpectedly have a sharp muscle pain that runs down her arms, hands, and legs. This intense pain can last between 30 seconds and 3 minutes. Her muscles twitch under her eyes and in her fingers, upper arms, and thighs. One week these symptoms can occur several times and the next week not at all. Her voice also has a fast, low pitch. One MRI has shown white lesions on her brain, but a second showed none. Doctors are stumped and have tentatively diagnosed her as having MS.

Reading: Thousands of white crystals form on her brain (or pass over the top of her brain) and seep into her body, disrupting the natural flow of her nervous system. These crystals have the appearance of rain falling gently, covering and then saturating her muscles before being absorbed by the cells. This is why one MRI found them and the second did not.

She was born with abnormal adrenal glands, with one barely developed and the other of a more normal size. This adrenal dysfunction is causing this unusual chemical release. She needs to see an endocrinologist. If her adrenal glands are not diseased and are in fact developed sufficiently, this problem may be treatable.

NECK/SHOULDER DISCOMFORT

F 44 yrs 10-19-98

Problem: She has periodic cracking sounds in her neck.

Reading: The noise in her neck is a ligament; she needs more vitamin E. (She confirmed in a follow-up call that the noise in her neck was diagnosed as a ligament problem.)

F 62 yrs 12-20-98

Problem: She has an achy and weak neck, shoulders, and arms. Doctors have been unable to diagnose the cause.

Reading: This is nerve-related. One area of concern is the base of the neck toward the front. It should be treated with Rolfing, massage, or reflexology. Rolfing should extend from up under the jaw down the front and sides of the neck, into the clavicle, upper chest, and front portions of the trapezius muscles.

F 58 yrs 02-21-00

Problem: She has had a stiff and painful neck and shoulders and a jabbing pain in the upper left side of the chest for the past 2 weeks.

Reading: The pain in her chest, neck, and shoulders is the result of tight trapezius muscles. This is caused by stress and a lack of exercise. She needs yoga for mind and body connection.

F 55 yrs 04-10-00

Problem: She has pain in the shoulder blades and neck. She is depressed and has been diagnosed with post-polio syndrome.

Reading: Her neck muscles are tight. She needs to take minerals to soften the tissues and then have a neck adjustment. The shoulder pain seems to be more polio-related. She needs a 40% improvement in her depression, which will help the polio problem. Acupuncture will help the depression.

F 46 yrs 12-29-99

Problem: She has neck and shoulder pain. The curvature has changed in her neck, and she has trouble sleeping because of the neck pain.
Reading: The first vertebra in her neck is borderline bulging. Rolfing would help this problem. The last cervical vertebra has compression, and this is soft-tissue–related. She needs stress-reduction therapies.

F 40 yrs 06-07-01

Problem: Over 20 years ago she began feeling a pain in the base of her neck that sometimes travels down the shoulder and arm. It has become worse over the years and is now chronic, although she still has range of motion. Chiropractors say that her lower cervical disk is degenerating, and they adjust it periodically but it does not help.
Reading: Soft tissue—a ligament high in the neck—is what she is feeling; it is calcified (arthritic) and she also has the structural problem at the cervical disk identified by her chiropractor. She needs Rolfing or acupuncture to the upper neck and upper back. The cervical disk should not be adjusted for now but rather Rolfed or acupunctured.

NERVE-BRAIN DISORDERS

M 34 yrs 05-24-99

Problem: He has anxiety attacks that occur when he is extremely tired.

He has had trouble sleeping for most of his life. He sleeps only 3 to 5 hours a night. Tests for sleeping disorders have been negative. He has bad dreams and sleepwalks. He wakes up sweating and hyperventilating and cannot determine if he has had a dream or if it was real.

Reading: He has had a nerve dysfunction since childhood that separates the left brain from the right brain more than normal. It may have happened during childbirth or at a young age when he suffered some form of head trauma. This nerve runs from the top center of his head through the center of his face and throat and stops at the base of his neck or upper chest. Medication will not help. He needs reflexology to restore the nerve and energy work to open up his forehead. This combination should eliminate the anxiety attacks.

M 4 yrs 08-27-00

Problem: He is moody and screams a lot. He can be charming one moment, and then he may relieve himself in his pants the next moment. He suffered a concussion when he was 18 months old and is very accident-prone. He has problems with his visual perception. His parents take him to a naturopath who treats him nutritionally.

Reading: He does not have a mental or physical illness. He may have a learning disability and nerve disorder and possibly attention-deficit disorder (ADD). He gets confused and frustrated when trying to figure things out and should work on one thought and subject at a time. If he can be taught to overcome this, he can grow out of this disorder. He needs attention, not discipline, and more exercise and focus. The nerve to the brain should be treated with reflexology. Food is not an issue, nor is the concussion an issue or a cause of his existing problems. Glasses help the vision but not the brain disorder. A practitioner such as a naturopath should focus on energy work and acupuncture for the brain disorder and not so much on diet.

M 59 yrs 02-05-01

Problem: He was diagnosed with bipolar disorder. He was adopted at 2 years of age.

Reading: The center of his head (the "soft spot" in newborns) is the main cause of his bipolar condition or nerve disorder. A nerve in this area zigzags outward to the top edge of the head and downward across both eyes into the upper cheeks. His condition is mild. Treatment by acupuncture to the top of head will help his condition improve.

M 54 yrs 01-27-01

Problem: He has had light-headedness with loss of balance for 6 months. His neurologist believes that he may have diabetes. He now suffers headaches and numbness in the right side of his head, and he is very tired.

Reading: He has a "V"-shaped, deep energy blockage on the top of his head, and he appears to have a nerve-brain disorder. This is a disruption caused by electrical airwaves, perhaps from mobile phones, antennas, or high-power voltage. He has an 80% chance of total recovery if exposure is eliminated. He will continue to get worse if he does not eliminate the exposure. He needs to open up energy from the navel up and out through the digestive system, lungs, chest, and shoulders. This will prevent any disorder in the future. He needs acupuncture to the brain for the nerve disorder and acupuncture to the body for energy. (He then explained that he works at the airport, where there are many electronic waves.)

F 57 yrs 09-04-00

Problem: She had a head injury 2 years ago and now has a slight head tremor.

Reading: She gives the impression of having epilepsy, but she more likely has a nerve disorder in the brain. She should see a neurologist for medication, and she would be helped by acupuncture. She will have this condition for the rest of her life, but it will not become severe.

F 39 yrs 01-20-01

Problem: She is tired and lacks energy. She is being treated with vitamins and herbs and is feeling a little better after treatment.

Reading: Her nervous system is the issue, and she should see a neurologist for an opinion. Two dark lines running up from the temples to the top of her head do not meet together. This is likely a nerve problem in the brain. She should try reflexology for 60 days, and if there is no improvement, she should then try acupuncture. With daily treatments, she should see a 40% improvement. She will, however, have this disorder for the rest of her life, and she will need treatments for the rest of her life. She needs to decrease the amount of vitamins that she is taking to avoid harming her liver. Perhaps she would be better off taking them in liquid form.

M 49 yrs 02-17-01

Problem: He has had many different and rare diseases diagnosed in the last 10 years, including diabetes insipidus, disk degeneration, a bone disease, and a brain disorder. He takes morphine and codeine daily for pain. He wants to know how this happened. He had head trauma 17 years ago and questions if that was the cause.

Reading: From one temple to the other he appears to have a wet-looking exposure to an electrical stimulation. His thyroid gland is hyperactive as a reaction to this exposure. (He said that he had been electrocuted 20 years earlier.) This electricity traveled first through his brain, then down through the thyroid gland, crossing in an X-fashion through the chest, and out through the male organs and thighs. He looks as though he is standing in place shocked and cannot stop trembling because of the electricity. He has been left with a nerve disorder that looks as though it could be reversed with electrical stimulation to the center of the brain (i.e., perhaps shocking him again would stop the trembling).

F 58 yrs 06-10-01

Problem: She has had a sharp pain for 30 years under the right ribcage that increases in the afternoon and is somewhat relieved when she lies down. Although diagnostic tests have been negative, doctors believe that her problem may be centered in her stomach. The pain can stay for 2 days and then disappear for a week. She once had a lot of energy but now it is greatly diminished.

Reading: The problem could be a result of a head injury or trauma to the brain–perhaps an injury to the vagus nerve or a nerve connected to the stomach or digestive tract. (She said that she had been a bull rider and suffered many head injuries and concussions.) She should have acupuncture to the vagus nerve in the brain.

F 43 yrs 06-28-01
Problem: Her spine has become twisted and out of alignment at the hip level, and because of this one leg is now shorter than the other. Three months ago she began getting headaches that have become chronic. She had a nerve block, but it has not helped.
Reading: She has a nerve disorder on one side of her brain that runs horizontally from just above the ear canal. This has affected the leg and foot on the same side of the body with the brain disorder. Her body has become twisted because the portion of the brain that controls the muscles is not receiving the correct messages, and as a result the muscles have no direction or command. This disorder is now causing head-aches. This nerve-brain disorder is related in some way to her ear canal. Treatment needs to focus on the ear canal and the nerves and area of the brain just above the ear. She might have had a virus that affected or damaged the nerves in the ear or brain. She should see an ear specialist.

NUMBNESS

F 81 yrs 05-15-00
Problem: She has lower back pain, and her feet are numb and ice cold. She is taking a thyroid hormone, but her last thyroid test was normal.
Reading: Her first and fifth lumbar disks are arthritic, along with the last cervical disk in her neck. She could use more minerals and exercise.

F 78 yrs 03-08-99
Problem: Her hands, feet, and right leg go numb. She also gets dizzy spells, which to her feel like a lack of circulation. An MRI was negative.
Reading: She does not have major nerve or circulation problems. Her main problem is her blood, which is low in minerals–particularly potassium and sodium. This is why she is dizzy as well. She should see a naturopath for mineral replacement.

M 52 yrs 04-14-98
Problem: Her thumb and index finger go numb.
Reading: The fifth and sixth cervical disks are fused together, causing the numbness in her thumb and index finger. Most of the problem is coming from the last cervical disk or head of the rib. This area needs adjustment, and the trapezius muscles need therapy because they are very tight. These treatments will help alleviate the numbness. Swimming would be a good overall exercise for him, and it would help relieve pressure on his neck.

F 58 yrs 02-21-00
Problem: Her left leg goes numb, and a nerve in her back is pinched.
Reading: Daily exercise and diaphragmatic breathing will improve the nerve, which will alleviate the numbness in her leg.

F 56 yrs 04-28-01
Problem: She was diagnosed with fibromyalgia 8 years ago for which she is taking medication. She also has numbness in her fingers and hands, right foot, and left heel, which began after she fell and broke her foot. This numbness has been diagnosed as a neuropathy.
Reading: Her cranium has moved forward slightly, and this is interfering with a gland–probably the hypothalamus–in the front portion of her brain. This gland cannot function properly and is the reason for the fibromyalgia and numbness. Cranial massage would help move the cranium. Then she should have acupuncture to stimulate the hypothalamus.

OSTEOPOROSIS

F 47 yrs 10-26-98
Problem: She was diagnosed with an underactive thyroid gland 10 years ago and with osteoporosis 4 years ago. She is on hormone replacement therapy and calcium and exercises for the osteoporosis. She is concerned about her adrenal glands as well.
Reading: Her thymus and pituitary glands need stimulation, not the thyroid and adrenal glands. The pituitary gland is shut down because of stress. She needs energy work and reflexology to stimulate the gland. Energy blockage starts at the base of her neck by the clavicle and runs to the back of the jaw behind her ear and up along the side of the head. Opening up this blocked energy will increase the blood and oxygen flow to the brain, which in turn will create more energy and stimulation to the pituitary gland. This pituitary gland problem is contributing to the thinning of her bones because of the hormones it controls. Her body is not absorbing the medication or calcium the way it should, possibly because the lungs are not allowing it. The lungs have an unwanted gas in them that is interfering with absorption of the medications.

F 51 yrs 08-06-99
Problem: She wants a general health reading.
Reading: She needs to monitor bone loss. This will show up as pain in one knee at first, and then in the hip area. She needs to keep up on her calcium intake and increase her potassium intake. Drinking apple cider vinegar would help.

F 64 yrs 04-03-00
Problem: She was diagnosed with bone loss in her hips.
Reading: The bone loss and hip pain are linked to her low hormone level and lack of exercise.

F 38 yrs 01-07-00
Problem: She is in early stages of osteoporosis.
Reading: The osteoporosis is caused by a lack of exercise and an energy blockage. She has a light gray energy shutdown from the top of her head to her feet. The energy needs to be worked in a "V"-shape, starting at the navel and moved upward and outward. The "V" should then be worked inward 1 inch at a time until the energy is moving straight up through her chest and neck.

F 48 yrs 09-05-01
Problem: She has had three back surgeries for ruptured disks, but she still has upper and lower back pain as well as pain in her hip. She no longer wants to work and has gained 50 pounds from just lying around.
Reading: Lack of exercise and weight gain are major factors in her back pain. Her hormones are slightly low because of inactivity and age, and this is causing her bones to become thin and soft. She might only need exercise, but she could increase her hormones as well. She lacks the will or desire to improve her health and is depressed about her personal life. She needs positive reinforcement and friends who enjoy exercise, walking, hiking, and sports.

PAIN

F 42 yrs 08-27-99

Problem: She has had pelvic, hip, and abdominal pain for the last 8 months. The pain moves from her back to her front. She fell 15 years earlier and believes that it may be related to the pain she has today. She is also depressed.

Reading: The pain is blood-related, not skeletal. She has pain and pressure in the front of her face, and her eyes are dark and burn. The blood appears to have a virus or infection that has settled in her lower torso area but runs up through the center of her chest and throughout the entire body. She will begin to suffer from joint pain, and her energy and appetite will deteriorate by the week if this problem is not corrected. A naturopath might treat her blood and digestive disorder with herbs to improve her enzymes, which have been depleted by the virus. Her depression will improve by 70% if her physical pain is corrected. Acupuncture to her face would also improve her depression. (She called a month later to say that her pelvic pain had already been reduced.)

F 60 yrs 07-05-99

Problem: She sleeps 9 hours a day. She wakes up with pain and does not want to get up. One day it might be in her legs and the next day in her chest. She is now on an antidepressant. She has undergone physical therapy for 20 years.

Reading: She has had a physical disorder for so many years that it has now affected her emotionally. The problem is a nerve that starts at the back of the head and runs down through the back of the neck and into her armpit. She wakes up with different parts of her body hurting because the nerve in the back of her head signals the body and then her muscles react accordingly. This is a soft tissue problem, not skeletal. This nerve is also affecting the pituitary gland. She needs reflexology to restore the area. She is on many different types of medication. Some of her diagnoses are correct, but others are not. The nerve disorder needs to be treated first, and then the medications can be adjusted.

F 55 yrs 01-07-00

Problem: She has headaches, back pain, hip pain, and pain in the bottoms of her feet. She believes that her pain was brought on by car accidents and that the only thing that will help her hip pain is surgery. Until she has the hip surgery she will not believe that doctors can help her.

Reading: She is low in minerals, especially potassium. She also needs enzymes for her digestive tract. Half of her body pain is physical, and the other half is emotional. Something is keeping her from wanting to get completely better. Eating according to her blood type would be beneficial to her and would help eliminate some of the toxins in her blood. This would also reduce the back and hip pain. She should practice self-hypnosis and diaphragmatic breathing. Once the dietary changes and supplements improve her back and hip pain, she may then come around emotionally and regain faith in her physicians.

F 21 yrs 09-21-98

Problem: She suffers from a crippling disease and is currently in a wheelchair. Doctors have not been able to help her, and she is in chronic pain.

Reading: Her condition likely was caused by trauma. (She then stated that she had been in three accidents several years ago, all within 3 months.) She is handling it better than she thinks she is, but her main problem is that she has not fully accepted this illness emotionally. She needs to work on this because it is the key to her healing. Once she has fully accepted this illness as just something that has happened to her, then she can begin to attack it physically. She should see a psychotherapist to start this emotional healing and then have some energy work done. She has an energy blockage that starts about 2 inches from the top of her forehead and runs straight down into her digestive tract. She needs to increase her vegetable intake but in a liquid form because her body cannot digest them in solid form. She also needs to increase her potassium intake. She should lie flat on her back as much as possible, with her head flat on the floor. She can put something under her feet if that feels better, but the rest of her body needs to be flat. This will help open up the energy in her body and, in turn, help her digestive system. She is also prone to urinary tract infections; increasing her water intake will help.

F 49 yrs 03-17-97

Problem: She was in a car accident 10 years ago and now walks with a cane. She has had a transcutaneous electrical nerve stimulator (TENS) unit implanted in the middle of her back. She wants to know what will help with her physical and emotional pain.

Reading: She needs to forget about the accident and stop trying to figure out why it happened to her. Her health is better than she thinks. She needs to use her time to her advantage and focus on her strengths— her mind, eyes, arms, and hands. Working with indoor plants, sewing, meditating, ad relaxing (but not too much) would be good for her. She might try getting Rolfed. Her chest gets tight with stress when she worries about her health. Putting stress on her heart by worrying could lead to other health problems. Brighter days are ahead if she would only change her thinking. She is in control of her health, more so than the doctors. Her health can improve or get worse; it is mostly up to her.

F 63 yrs 10-11-01

Problem: She was diagnosed with fibromyalgia and has had 8 years of chronic body pain. Her legs are her biggest problem—she can walk only a few steps at a time. She has a rare red blood cell (RBC) disorder, and doctors believe that this is causing her leg problems. She is also very fatigued and unable to work because of her condition.

Reading: The lining of her lungs looks irregular, as though she were exposed to a chemical burn or smoke inhalation. This has prevented her lungs from filtering blood properly and resulted in her blood being poisoned. Blood passing through the digestive tract is not much better, and by the time it reaches her legs it is in its worst condition, with the RBCs nearly depleted. Her lung condition has caused both the RBC disorder and the fibromyalgia. She needs to increase the oxygen level in her blood. (She then stated that she has been smoking since she was a little girl.)

PANCREATIC PROBLEMS

F 27 yrs 05-08-00
Problem: She has had irregular menstrual periods for 13 years. For 3 years she has had an itchy skin rash that resembles hives.

Reading: Both her liver and pancreas are toxic and are linked to the irregular periods and the rash. Fried foods are the cause. Both organs need to be flushed with herbs, and she might see a naturopath for this treatment.

M 53 yrs 04-24-00
Problem: He has had three stents put in his coronary artery in the last 2 years but still suffers from mild chest pain. Tests are negative, and doctors say it is indigestion.

Reading: The chest pain is coming from the back side of the heart. The problem is too much cholesterol in his blood. The source of the problem is probably the pancreas, which is functioning abnormally and contributing to the cholesterol problem. About 60% of the cause of his abnormally functioning pancreas is stress.

F 49 yrs 12-13-99

Problem: She is concerned about her high cholesterol level and its possible effects on her heart.

Reading: She is a strong candidate for eating according to her blood type. Her pancreas has been the most affected by her diet. She needs to cleanse her pancreas and have energy work to the pancreas and gallbladder because she has an energy block to these areas up through the colon, chest, neck, and face. She is also susceptible to diabetes. The blood-type diet should help prevent diabetes and control her cholesterol level.

F 3 yrs 12-02-99

Problem: She has had digestive problems since birth and was diagnosed with malabsorption (inability to absorb nutrients). She has trouble gaining weight and is now on a hypoallergenic diet.

Reading: The pancreas appears to be the main problem, and it has affected her liver and perhaps her gallbladder and upper colon. She needs digestive enzymes and more vitamins and minerals. Acupuncture or reflexology should be used to stimulate the pancreas. The strict diet is not a cure, although it is helping her from becoming worse. However, it appears to be robbing her of some nutrients. Supplements would help.

F 54 yrs 12-30-00

Problem: She was diagnosed with Sjögren's syndrome, an autoimmune disease in which the eyes, mouth, and sinuses are chronically dry.

Reading: Her pituitary gland and pancreas are two major factors in her Sjögren's syndrome. This is a hormonal and digestive issue. If her hormones are balanced, 60% of the dryness will improve.

PARASITES

F 27 yrs 04-02-98
Problem: She was diagnosed with lupus a year earlier. She is being treated with an antimalaria medicine, which has suppressed the disease symptoms.
Reading: Her gallbladder, spleen, liver, and maybe the stomach should be checked for parasites, and a naturopathic doctor could explain how to cleanse these organs. They are not functioning properly, because of either a parasite or blood problem. The blood looks toxic and lacks oxygen, and the blood cells appear to be infected. This is in an advanced stage but not yet to the point where it cannot be helped.

F 70 yrs 10-13-98
Problem: She has very dry skin.
Reading: She is low in vitamins and minerals, especially zinc. She likely has a parasite in the lining of her colon, and for this reason the vitamins and minerals are not being processed throughout her body. The liver is overloaded from having to deal with this parasite. This low level of vitamins and minerals is causing the dry skin.

M 29 yrs 05-08-00
Problem: For the past 2 weeks he has had blood in his stool, vomiting, and bowel movements four to six times every morning.
Reading: He also has a hard time gaining weight and likely has a parasite. He needs to flush his liver and avoid alcohol.

F 28 yrs 10-22-99
Problem: She has been ill with gastrointestinal problems for 3 years.

Since then she has had low energy and frequent colds, flu, and strep throats.

Reading: Her ascending and descending colon are the main cause of the low energy, flu, and colds. She needs to start with a colonic enema and then have reflexology and herbs for the digestion. She might have a parasite or blood disorder. Her blood looks dark red and thick and lacking in oxygen as well.

F 49 yrs 08-26-97

Problem: Her gallbladder was removed, and doctors do not like the way the tissue looks.

Reading: The tissue looks bad because it had parasites—some of them alive and some dead. The parasites have been there for quite some time—a lot of dead and infected tissue is present. This should start to cause her stomach pain. The large intestine is affected, and it is spreading. It could be a rare form of parasite. It will or has already entered the bloodstream and begun to affect her heart. The outcome does not look good. It needs to be caught and treated now, although it already may be well advanced.

F 39 yrs 07-19-98

Problem: She has reflex sympathetic dystrophy, a nerve disease. She has uncontrollable pain and seems to be getting progressively worse.

Reading: She should see a naturopathic physician for an oxygenation supplement because her blood needs more oxygen and may have a parasite.

F 35 yrs 07-15-01

Problem: She was diagnosed 5 years ago with diffuse interstitial lung fibrosis. Her lungs are stiff and do not expand properly when she breathes. This condition is expected to worsen as she ages and could result in her death. She also has migraine headaches, dizziness, narcolepsy, and seizure-type symptoms. Doctors do not know what caused this disease, although birds and chemicals are commonly implicated.

Reading: A parasite is the cause of her symptoms. Eliminating the parasite should improve her condition except for the lung problem. For the lungs she needs deep upper shoulder and back massage with herbal oils. This oil should be left on the body for optimal absorption. This massage, along with acupuncture to the lungs, should help the fibrosis.

PARKINSON'S DISEASE

F 53 yrs 07-16-01
Problem: She was diagnosed with Parkinson's disease 3 years ago. Medication helps control her twitching, although stress tends to make it worse. At times she also has esophageal reflux. She wants to know what she can do to cope with these problems.

Reading: An animal bite–possibly from a rabid animal–caused a blood reaction in her body, which caused heavy metals in her blood to react to the infection. This reaction disrupted the nerves in her head, causing the twitching and parkinsonism, which in turn is causing the reflux. (She stated that a squirrel bit her when she was 9 years of age.) She needs acupuncture for her brain area and toxins removed from her blood. She should also eat according to her blood type and avoid foods that make her blood more toxic, such as those containing yeast and other fungi.

PITUITARY GLAND PROBLEMS

F 35 yrs 11-19-99
Problem: Her breasts are undergoing lactation but she is not pregnant. Doctors have been treating this condition with herbs.
Reading: This problem is caused by her pituitary gland.

F 38 yrs 12-02-99
Problem: She was recently diagnosed with a benign breast lump; a test revealed calcium deposits in the lump. She also has gum problems.
Reading: The pituitary gland looks exhausted and is a factor in the gum and breast problems. She needs to learn how to relax and meditate, and this will help the pituitary.

M 40 yrs 01-24-99
Problem: He suffers from a lack of sleep. His memory is poor, and he gets confused when trying to make a decision.
Reading: His lack of sleep is caused by "jump starting" his dominant gland—the pituitary—with sugar, caffeine, and chocolate after noon. He needs to take an herb that will help restore the pituitary gland.

F 47 yrs 10-26-98
Problem: She was diagnosed 10 years ago with an underactive thyroid gland and 4 years ago with osteoporosis. She takes hormones and calcium and exercises for the osteoporosis. She is concerned about her adrenal glands as well.
Reading: Her thymus and pituitary glands need stimulation rather than

the thyroid and adrenal glands. The pituitary gland is shut down because of her stress. She needs reflexology and other energy work to stimulate the gland. Energy blockage starts at the base of her neck and runs up the side of the neck to the back of the jaw, behind the ear, and up along the side of her head. Opening up this blocked energy will increase blood and oxygen flow to the brain, which in turn will create more energy and stimulation to the pituitary gland. The pituitary gland problem is contributing to the thinning of the bones because of the hormones it controls.

F 27 yrs 04-05-99

Problem: Her naturopathic doctor believes that she has too much mercury in her teeth. Recently she has been losing a lot of hair. She has pain in her ankles, hands, knees, jaw, and neck. She has been diagnosed with lupus.

Reading: The naturopathic doctor is correct about the high mercury level in her bloodstream. It is causing the joint pain, along with high levels of other minerals such as copper and aluminum. She has been under stress, and her brain has been releasing (or overproducing) minerals, most likely a result of the dysfunctional pituitary gland. The pituitary should be treated with reflexology, and she needs to learn stress-release techniques, perhaps through hypnosis tapes. The hair loss and acne are also linked to the problems with her pituitary gland. Most likely she does not have lupus.

F 59 yrs 07-24-00

Reading: She was diagnosed in April with under-active thyroid and adrenal glands. For many years she has suffered from kidney disease and had a kidney removed. She also has difficulty sleeping and is frequently nauseated.

Reading: Her hormones and pituitary gland are the two main issues. First she needs to stabilize the pituitary gland and then balance her hormones. The sleeping disorder is hormone-related, not dietary or stress-related. She is prone to dehydration and must drink fluids to avoid more kidney problems. Her pituitary gland is the main factor in her kidney disease and the cause of the loss of her kidney.

F 31 yrs 06-02-00
Problem: Her menstrual periods have been irregular for the past 4 to 5 months.
Reading: Her female hormones are okay, but the pituitary gland needs to be checked. Her stress level is affecting the pituitary gland.

F 54 yrs 08-20-00
Problem: She wonders if she has multiple sclerosis (MS).
Reading: The backside of the pituitary gland is slightly enlarged. This is a reaction to a nerve disorder perhaps caused by medication that she was given when she had surgery. She does not have MS, but she does have a mild nerve disease that is most likely not going to get worse nor ever be identified. She also needs acupuncture and homeopathic remedies for the pituitary and thyroid glands.

F 35 yrs 07-06-99
Problem: Her breasts are lactating.
Reading: The base of her throat is swollen, caused by a soft tissue trauma. (She then explained that she had a whiplash injury 2 months earlier.) The pituitary gland suffered trauma and it is not functioning normally, which is why her breasts are lactating. This can be corrected by treating the pituitary gland with energy work such as acupuncture.

F 40 yrs 11-21-00
Problem: She has pain and tenderness in her breasts. She also is concerned that she sleeps too much.
Reading: Her breasts are tender because her pituitary gland is exhausted and has affected the release of her hormones. Reflexology and herbs would help her. She could suffer damage to the breast ducts in 5 years if this problem persists.

F 51 yrs 02-09-01

Problem: She has experienced several months of pain on the right side of her body.

Reading: Her pituitary gland is causing a hormone imbalance. She is sensitive to touch on her body and is borderline for fibromyalgia. However, the fibromyalgia can be prevented by balancing her hormones, in particular those governed by the pituitary gland. Stress has caused the pituitary problem.

F 38 yrs 09-25-00

Problem: She has depression that has occurred off and on for years. At times she has to force herself to leave her house. She has been off medication for 8 months and is doing okay without it.

Reading: An energy block over the front of her face is causing this depression and her pituitary gland to be weak. Acupuncture would help her.

F 40 yrs 02-25-01

Problem: She was diagnosed 3 years ago with a benign pituitary gland tumor. Doctors decided to leave the tumor and treat her with medications. She is concerned because her family has a history of cancer.

Reading: She needs to stop drinking dark-colored carbonated soft drinks. These drinks have affected her pituitary gland and are the likely cause of the tumor.

F 51 yrs 05-14-01

Problem: She has had sore throats for 30 years, mainly when she gets cold. Throat cultures are always negative, although she does have swollen glands and sinus drainage. She is on medication that helps a little. When she works around the house, she sweats so profusely she has to change clothes at least 10 times a day. If she sits still, she gets ice cold. This has been happening for 10 years. The cold and sweating worsened after a hysterectomy 5 years ago.

Reading: The cause of the hypothermia, sweating, and sore throat is the pituitary gland. It needs stimulation via reflexology and acupuncture. She also needs to see an endocrinologist for medication. The cause of the sinus drainage is not clear–perhaps it is the pituitary gland as well.

M 50 yrs 07-07-01
Problem: He has tremors mainly in his head and hands. He believes that they are hereditary because his mother had them.
Reading: His pituitary gland is the cause of his shaking. It is not functioning normally and is affecting his brain, which in turn is causing the tremors. The gland should be treated with acupuncture or reflexology.

F 54 yrs 10-18-01
Problem: She has had dry eyes for 15 years. Eye drops do not help, and doctors do not know what to do for her. She also has rosacea, a chronic skin condition. She has had much stress in her personal life.
Reading: Her pituitary gland is the cause of her dry eyes. It is not releasing enough hormone. This is stress-related and also is the cause of her rosacea. She should seek treatment for her pituitary gland, which should improve her eye and skin problems.

PSORIASIS

M 40 yrs 01-24-99
Problem: He has psoriasis and believes that it is related to his stress. He has had outbreaks throughout the years during periods of stress.
Reading: His psoriasis is 60% stress-related and 40% diet-related. He should avoid sugar, caffeine, and chocolate and work with a therapist regarding his stress level.

M 24 yrs 04-03-96
Problem: He has psoriasis.
Reading: He must sleep 8 hours a night and go to bed and get up at the same time daily. This consistent sleeping pattern will help him control the psoriasis and prevent it from getting worse. He also should avoid fried foods and alcohol.

F 51 yrs 02-12-01
Problem: She has had chronically inflamed psoriasis for 10 years. The breakouts are on her buttocks, stomach, legs, and arms but not on her face. It is worse in the evenings and when she is under stress. She is being treated for it but with poor results.
Reading: The spleen is most likely the cause of the psoriasis. It looks clogged and fat engorged. Energy can be opened to the spleen with acupuncture and reflexology.

M 40 yrs 06-18-01
Problem: He has had psoriasis all over his body for the past 20 years. Sun seems to help him, and summers are better than winter. He uses over-the-counter medications to treat the problem.
Reading: His pancreas and colon are factors in the psoriasis. The colon is sluggish, and foods have become backed up, causing his blood to be toxic. Flushing the colon with herbs, diet, and even colonic enemas would help. His diet is bothering his colon, which in turn is bothering his psoriasis, and the pancreas ultimately is the cause of both.

M 60 yrs 02-10-01
Problem: He has psoriasis and is worried that he may have skin cancer as well.
Reading: His liver is toxic and is causing the age spots and psoriasis. He should drink apple cider vinegar to detoxify his liver. He does not have skin cancer, but he needs to work on his liver.

RADIATION EXPOSURE

F 54 yrs 08-20-00

Problem: She had a benign tumor on her thyroid gland removed and has nerve damage as a result. She wonders if she has multiple sclerosis (MS).

Reading: She does not have MS. The thyroid tumor developed as a reaction to radiation exposure. Although most of her thyroid gland was removed, the remaining gland could still form more benign lumps. The remaining thyroid gland and the thymus gland need to be stimulated via reflexology.

F 55 yrs 02-01-99

Problem: She wants a general health reading.

Reading: Her thyroid gland is beginning to malfunction and needs energy work. This may be all the thyroid gland needs, but she may have waited too long. She should ask an older sibling if she was exposed to radiation or dangerous chemicals as a child.

F 54 yrs 03-15-99

Problem: She has a history of digestive disorders, including gas and bloating in the colon. She has been diagnosed with celiac disease (gluten intolerance).

Reading: She has a blockage to her colon. She needs energy work on the colon, upper stomach, liver, and gallbladder straight up through the center of the chest. She should also take an herbal enzyme. The colon's enzymes are depleted because of radiation exposure, and she needs to detoxify from the radiation.

M 66 yrs 03-06-01

Problem: He was diagnosed with prostate cancer 3 years ago and underwent radiation treatments. He wants to know if they stopped the cancer. He has also been experiencing some rectal bleeding.

Reading: The prostate looks okay. He has a little bleeding in the rectum and colon caused by the radiation treatments, but this should heal in time. Diet would be important for this as well. He has an energy blockage in the small intestine, rectum, and prostate gland because of the radiation treatments. Acupuncture or reflexology to these areas would help correct this.

F 41 yrs 05-06-01

Problem: She has had health problems for the past 27 years. She does not know what is wrong, but she believes that it may be emotionally caused. When she was 14 years of age she was diagnosed with Hodgkin's disease. She was treated surgically and with radiation. Then she underwent a thyroidectomy because her thyroid gland was damaged by the radiation. Now she has left breast cancer, and her estrogen level is very high.

Reading: Her thymus gland is not holding energy. Energy enters the thymus and moves right through it and out the back of her neck. This is a result of her radiation treatments. They burned a hole in the gland. The hole in the gland needs to be closed with acupuncture and herbs, and this should enable the body to hold onto its energy and come back into balance.

F 70 yrs 08-06-01

Problem: She can hear her heart beat. Sometimes it seems so loud to her that she thinks others can hear it. Doctors believe it is psychological. This began 7 years ago during radiation treatments for bone cancer. Because of radiation she also has sporadic diarrhea. She also feels her eyes "jump." She had more radiation treatments for breast cancer 2 years ago.

Reading: She has a reversal of energy flow. It is running upward rather than downward and out through the feet in the way energy flow usually travels. With the blood being forced upward into her head, she then can hear the pulse from her heart. This reversal of energy flow has thrown her body and immune system off and made her vulnerable to illnesses such as cancer. She needs full-body energy work that will move her energy downward, not upward, and clockwise rather than counter-clockwise. Her radiation treatments likely were the cause of her energy reversal.

F 50 yrs 08-09-01
Problem: She has a low white blood cell (WBC) count. Doctors do not know why this has occurred, but they suspect that a virus is the cause. She lacks energy and has no resistance to infection.
Reading: Radiation treatment disrupted her adrenal glands and altered her WBC count. Because her adrenal glands are exhausted, her energy is very low. Even her lungs are involved. She needs reflexology for her lungs and adrenal glands and acupuncture and herbs for her adrenal glands.

REPRODUCTIVE/SEXUAL ISSUES

M 62 yrs 06-08-99
Problem: He has erection difficulties.
Reading: About 70% of his problem achieving an erection is physical, and acupuncture would help this function. The other 30% is emotional.

F 37 yrs 10-09-97
Problem: She has discomfort during intercourse.

Reading: Emotionally she feels that she is going to become a victim of something, either an assault or rape. She does not have confidence in men or in relationships. Her pain is both mentally and physically caused. She may have been molested as a child. The reproductive area is dry and needs to be treated to enable lubrication. She might try a self-defense class, which will help in overcoming her fears of becoming a victim.

F 31 yrs 12-14-99

Problem: She has a difficult time becoming sexually stimulated.

Reading: The sexual disorder is 60% physical and 40% emotional. She needs to reset her priorities. Sex should be on her priority list. She also needs to stop using artificial objects for sexual arousal so that her mind does not expect or rely on them.

M 20 yrs 02-09-97

Problem: He has little sexual desire.

Reading: He has an energy blockage at the top of the chest that runs down through the body to the base of the penis. The penis coloration does not look good. He may have an infection or disease. His low sexual desire could be partly from cocaine use.

F 39 yrs 10-04-99

Problem: She has a low sex drive and is overweight.

Reading: Her low sex drive is mostly physical—she is too heavy. Her weight problem is mainly thyroid-related. Her thyroid gland is okay, but it is inactive. Acupuncture would help stimulate it. Salt is also influencing her weight because she is retaining water. She needs more protein, fewer carbohydrates, and more exercise. She also needs to drink more water.

M 39 yrs 09-13-99

Problem: His doctor wanted an opinion on the appropriate treatment for his patient's premature ejaculation. The doctor believes that it is a physical problem within the sex organs.

Reading: It is a physical problem that is nerve-related. Acupuncture would help. (Two weeks later the doctor reported that after the acupuncture the man could sustain an erection for 10 minutes before ejaculation.)

.

F 27 yrs 05-08-00

Problem: Her periods are irregular, but the flow is normal. She wonders if she is capable of pregnancy.

Reading: Both the liver and pancreas are toxic and are linked to the irregular periods. Fried foods are the cause. She needs to flush both organs with herbs. She can become pregnant, but her emotional state will slow it down. She is very concerned about her personal life.

F 57 yrs 09-04-00

Problem: She has had periodic yeast and bacterial infections in the vaginal area for the past 20 years. She experienced a salt-type burning to this area 2 weeks ago. She has had this problem before, but this was the most intense. Hormone supplements have not helped. Everything aggravates this area, including toilet tissue and creams.

Reading: She has an infection or blockage in the fallopian tube. (She then stated that she had a tubal ligation 20 years ago.) Having her tubes tied likely brought on the vaginal discomfort because of a lack of body fluids and important nutrients getting to this area. This is causing the salt-burning effects. Most likely she has scar tissue from having had this surgery. (She commented that when her tubes were tied she was given a large incision.)

F 51 yrs 02-12-01

Problem: She has a cyst on her ovary, but doctors do not seem concerned about it.

Reading: The cyst is not a problem. However, to prevent problems or more cysts, she needs to watch her blood. She might try a juice fast, and she should eat according to her blood type. Exercise would energize her lungs to help purify her blood.

M 54 yrs 05-12-01

Problem: He has been inactive sexually most of his life–he meditated instead. However, now he is in a sexual relationship, and even though sex is now important to him, his sex drive is very low. His heart feels tired after sex.

Reading: He has a disconnection from his head to his shoulders–an energy blockage in his neck–which is why he feels separated emotionally. This started when he was a young child because of a dominant parent. He needs to breathe using his diaphragm during and after sex to avoid fatigue. He is afraid to engage in sex and make a mistake, so he does not allow himself to relax. He should practice slowing down, enjoying sex, and breathing properly while he engages in it. He also needs to talk with his partner and make her an important part of their lovemaking. He needs to partake in the energy exchange that takes place during intercourse.

M 50 yrs 06-11-01

Problem: He recently turned 50 years of age and wants a general health reading. He is an occasional smoker and has undergone a lot of stress during the past 15 years.

Reading: His head is tilted forward and down, which is blocking energy to the frontal portions of the brain, forehead, one side of his face, and hypothalamus gland, causing him to be fatigued. Smoking is contributing to the energy shutdown to his forehead and face. The thymus gland has energy blockage as well and, along with his hypothalamus, is contributing to his low sex drive. He would benefit from Rolfing and cranial work to his head to move it back and centered over his neck. His neck should be Rolfed as well.

F 26 yrs 05-27-01

Problem: She began having sharp pains in the navel, down the right side, and occasionally on the left side 9 years ago. She once ran a fever for three months. Exploratory surgery revealed an ovarian cyst on her left side but no reason for the pain on her right side. Since the surgery her right leg goes numb. If she sits for more than 15 minutes the pain returns and the leg goes numb.

Reading: Her uterus appears to be set back too far, and her pelvic area is not in balance. This combination is causing the low abdominal pain and leg numbness. (She agrees that pelvic examinations cause horrible pain.) The uterine and pelvic areas should be Rolfed. Acupuncture would be a second option.

SCOLIOSIS

M 15 yrs 09-28-99

Problem: He has scoliosis and respiratory problems and uses an oxygen mask at night because he has a collapsed chest. He also weighs over twice what he should for his height.

Reading: The scoliosis is a big concern because it is so restrictive for him. Exercise and acupuncture could help improve his scoliosis and respiratory problems and even promote weight loss.

F 21 yrs 09-13-99

Problem: She has scoliosis.

Reading: The scoliosis is minor and not a setback, but it will get worse without exercise. She needs to exercise her legs, which will strengthen her back without putting direct pressure on it. Eating according to her blood type also would help her.

F 29 yrs 02-12-00

Problem: She has had scoliosis since childhood.

Reading: Soft tissue work is needed for the scoliosis. Acupuncture and Rolfing would be very beneficial, later using Rolfing for maintenance.

Diet and emotion are also factors. She is very sensitive to food and needs to eat according to her blood type, consuming the highly beneficial foods only. About 30% of her problem is emotional. Self-hypnosis would help. She is too serious and needs to relax.

F 68 yrs 06-04-01

Problem: She has scoliosis for which she wears a back brace all day. Her back pain is worse when standing. Thirty years ago her pain was in the upper back, but now it is in the lower back. Doctors do not know the cause. Three years ago she had heart attack symptoms, and surgeons put a stent in her right ventricle.

Reading: Her cigarette smoking has caused toxins to form in the blood, which is the key to her health issues for the last 30 years, including her lung problems, digestive disorder, and heart and bladder problems. (She then stated that even though she hadn't mentioned it at the beginning of the reading she has had colitis for years and has to wear panty liners because of bladder problems.). She needs reflexology or acupuncture to the lungs, colon, and bladder and to quit smoking. Her adrenal glands are causing the cravings for smoking.

SINUS PROBLEMS

M 7 yrs 12-03-99

Problem: He cries a lot. He is allergic to eggs and has had many antibiotics.

Reading: He suffers from sinus problems that cause headaches, which is why he cries. His allergies are airborne pollens, animal hair, dog, and cats. The sinus pressure causes his ears to clog and ring.

F 47 yrs 01-28-98
Problem: She believes that she has a major food allergy problem.
Reading: Her food sensitivities are not as bad as she or her doctors believe. She has allergies or sinus reactions over the center of her forehead and over both eyes and down the nose. She should avoid sugar because it irritates her sinuses. (She stated after the reading that she has recently been having headaches and was thinking it was the result of the sugar cravings.)

M 29 yrs 04-26-99
Problem: He has sinus problems.
Reading: He has sinus pressure caused by a lot of drainage in his throat and behind his cheekbones. Dairy products contribute to the drainage. This pressure has affected his thought processes as well.

F 56 yrs 11-18-99
Problem: She has long-term sinus congestion and is overweight.
Reading: The sinus congestion is mostly diet-related. Eating according to her blood type would help her sinuses and weight problem.

F 49 yrs 03-24-00
Problem: She has sinus discomfort.
Reading: Eating dairy products causes her sinus problem.

M 50 yrs 06-19-00
Problem: He has had two sinus surgeries and gets allergies and the flu frequently.
Reading: He needs a room air purifier for his sinuses.

F 54 yrs 09-30-98
Problem: She has chronic sinus irritation on one side of her face that flares up and is painful at times. Her upper gum area is irritated as well.
Reading: Her gum problem is related to her sinus condition. Homeopathic remedies would help both.

F 57 yrs 09-28-98
Problem: She has sinus discomfort.
Reading: Poor air quality and cigarette smoking cause her sinus problems. Cranial work by a practitioner of reflexology, chiropractic, and/or Rolfing would help her sinus condition.

F 38 yrs 03-07-96
Problem: Her sinuses are dry, and she sometimes has a bloody nose.
Reading: She has slight glandular swelling under the chin that is connected to her sinus problems. Her organs are very dry and lack moisture. She needs to drink more water to moisturize and flush her system.

M 53 yrs 03-12-01
Problem: He has been experiencing dizziness and pressure in his head for the past year. Although these symptoms are present at night, they are much more severe during the day. He has had many diagnostic tests, and they have all been negative.
Reading: One side of his sinus has an obstruction, possibly a tumor. Everything else looks fine. He needs to have his sinuses checked.

F 59 yrs 03-26-01
Problem: She was diagnosed with asthma 13 years ago and now has a chronic sinus problem. Steroids and antibiotics no longer seem to work. Four years ago she lost her sense of smell and had polyps removed in her sinus cavity. Doctors believe that another polyp deep in her sinuses is blocking her ability to smell.
Reading: Her thymus gland is affecting her lymphatic system and her sinus passages. Her asthma is also connected to the thymus gland. Acupuncture for her thymus gland will help these problems and may even restore her sense of smell.

F 61 yrs 04-25-01
Problem: She has had three sinus surgeries and wants to know what is causing her sinus problem.

Reading: Her thyroid gland is "off," and this is causing sugar cravings. If her thyroid gland were treated, she would have fewer sugar cravings, and this would help her sinus condition.

F 48 yrs 09-02-01

Problem: Her sinuses have been very dry for 18 years. Doctors have prescribed medications that she does not want to take.

Reading: Mineral deficiency–zinc, potassium, iron, and selenium–is the cause of her dry sinuses. She should see a naturopath or other physician for these minerals.

SKIN (DERMATOLOGIC) PROBLEMS

F 12 yrs 02-08-98

Problem: She was allergic to most chemicals and detergents when she was younger.

Reading: She is not overly allergic to much of anything–clogged pores cause her reactions. Most of her body is clogged, with the worst area under the arms. Her facial pores are also clogged. She needs to sweat (taking saunas frequently would be good) and drink plenty of water. She might use a warm, moist cloth over her face to open her pores.

F 59 yrs 04-10-98

Problem: Her hair lacks moisture and is slightly brittle. She has clogged pores in her scalp and believes that she may be allergic to her hair products. She is tender or sensitive on the outside of her forehead just above the ends of her eyebrows.

Reading: Chemicals or the environment may be the cause of her forehead tenderness. These chemicals affect the area around her eyes as well. She is also allergic to animals, dogs in particular. A room air purifier will help her more than anything else. She also needs to perspire.

F 40 yrs 10-05-98
Problem: She has skin eruptions.
Reading: She is intolerant of four food types. The spots on her face are related to a combination of high stress and eating one of the four food types to which she is intolerant. This combination causes her reaction.

F 62 yrs 12-20-98
Problem: Her skin itches so badly on her buttocks that it burns at times. She also has hip and leg aches.
Reading: These problems are nerve-related. The pain in her hips and legs is coming from the mid-lumbar area. Rolfing can help this. The source is a disk that has been slightly compressed and slipped forward, causing nerve interference.

F 61 yrs 10-01-98
Problem: She has very dry skin and hair.
Reading: She lacks vitamins and minerals. Her dry hair is also stress-related.

F 43 yrs 04-23-96
Problem: She has skin irritation, especially on the face.
Reading: Keeping her hands very clean will help the skin irritation around her mouth from spreading and may even help clear it up. The irritation is not nerve-or diet-related; it is germ-related.

M 48 yrs 06-29-99
Problem: He has red spots all over his body that come and go but mostly stay. He has extremely dry feet, and his toenails are yellow and thickened. These symptoms began 9 to 10 years ago.
Reading: His skin is dry and lacks elasticity. This problem might have

originated from an exposure to chemicals. (He then stated that 10 years ago he worked with chemicals.) Reflexology and acupuncture would help him. He also needs to keep his skin very clean and well lubricated.

M 43 yrs 05-18-97

Problem: He has very dry hair and skin.

Reading: His body is dry inside and out. He needs to increase his intake of potassium and other minerals, especially selenium, and use a sun block to protect his skin from the sun. He should detoxify his body with steam baths or saunas. He must also increase his water intake to three times the amount he currently consumes.

F 49 yrs 10-17-96

Problem: She has skin irritation and was diagnosed with a form of skin cancer.

Reading: She is having a toxic reaction, possibly caused by pesticide spray, dish soap, and laundry detergents. This reaction could even be airborne, and she may be reacting to the heavy air pollution. She wears a little too much makeup, which could be toxic or irritating to her skin. She needs to use less deodorant and perfume because they could be toxic to her. She might change the brand or use a natural type of deodorant. The overall toxic buildup may get worse if she does not get it under control. She might try saunas to sweat out the toxins in her body, and she needs to ensure that her clothes, bedclothes, and dishes are rinsed well. She should also drink purified water and breathe clean air. After making these changes she will respond positively and the problem will improve greatly.

F 46 yrs 05-08-00

Problem: She has age spots and is tired.

Reading: The age spots are caused by dry skin and diminished lung capacity. She is tired because of a lack of oxygen to the brain. The lower portion of her lungs looks 30% congested, probably from allergies, with cigarettes as a secondary cause. She might take dry saunas. She is also slightly low in minerals and should take potassium.

F 41 yrs 11-03-98

Problem: She is concerned about getting skin cancer because her sister died of it at 24 years of age.

Reading: Her state of mind is very important regarding whether she will get skin cancer. Her skin is most at risk with pesticides, followed by sun exposure and chlorine. She should avoid outdoor Jacuzzis with high concentrations of chlorine and watch her exposure to free radicals, which are formed in connection with air pollution and sunlight. She would benefit from selenium, a trace mineral that protects the skin from damage caused by free radicals.

F 78 yrs 07-09-99

Problem: She has red bumps all over her body. She believes that she is allergic to something. She also has had eczema on her hands for the past 5 years. She was at the Mayo Clinic for tests, but they came back negative.

Reading: Her adrenal glands are exhausted and appear to be, at least partially, the cause of the rash.

F 41 yrs 10-17-99

Problem: A urine test has revealed gallbladder, liver, kidney, adrenal, and digestive problems.

Reading: Her bones and soft tissue are dry. She needs dietary oils and potassium. Her hair is dry as well, and she should drink apple cider vinegar.

F 28 yrs 04-10-00

Problem: She has facial acne, and her nails are becoming weak.

Reading: The acne and nail problems are connected to her pituitary gland. Her pituitary gland is not releasing enough hormones, but it is not clear why.

M 30 yrs 07-08-00
Problem: He has age spots.
Reading: Selenium would be good for his skin spots and his toxic liver.

F 42 yrs 12-11-98
Problem: She has facial acne.
Reading: Clogged pores are the major cause of the acne, followed by diet. Eliminating yeast and starch from her diet would improve the acne.

F 45 yrs 01-31-99
Problem: She has cellulite.
Reading: Her thyroid gland is a factor in the increase of cellulite. It kicks off and on and fails to regulate itself throughout the day. Her hormones are affecting the thyroid gland, and this is anxiety-related. She might need a year before she finds a hormone balance and starts to feel better.

F 27 yrs 05-08-00
Problem: For 3 years she has had a warm and itchy skin rash that resembles hives. She also has irregular menstrual periods.
Reading: Both her liver and pancreas are toxic and linked to the irregular periods and the rash. Fried foods are the cause. She needs both organs flushed with herbs.

F 33 yrs 09-04-97
Problem: She is concerned about her complexion.
Reading: Stress is most likely causing her complexion to break out. She is on the go too much. She should read more to relax her mind and avoid focusing on unimportant issues.

F 57 yrs 10-06-98
Problem: A rash appeared on her neck 10 years ago. Sometimes it is bright red, and sometimes it fades.
Reading: This rash is related to the sweat glands in her neck, which

respond negatively to poor air quality and hot dry air and is the reason the rash is worse in the summer. In addition, the pores in her neck appear to be abnormal. Medication will not help, but cool water treatments will.

F 49 yrs 05-15-00
Problem: She had basal cell carcinomas (skin cancer) removed from her face, neck, and legs and is concerned about future growths.
Reading: The skin cancer is linked to vitamin and mineral loss, which in turn is related to her stress level.

M 47 yrs 03-14-99
Problem: His left index finger has been diagnosed with dermatitis. He has been taking medication, but it has not gotten better.
Reading: He has a virus that is dormant and then resurfaces with stress. He suffers from anxiety attacks. The doctor needs to draw blood to determine the type of virus or change the medication. The dermatitis can be controlled by diet, sleep, medication, and alleviation of emotional stress. This virus will become more dormant as the years pass. He may be sensitive to yeast, and he might try eating according to his blood type.

M 7 yrs 02-21-99
Problem: He has very dry skin.
Reading: The dry skin is caused by a lack of potassium and possible liver and kidney dysfunction. He needs to drink more water to flush his kidneys and take herbs to remove toxins from his liver.

F 70 yrs 10-13-98
Problem: She has very dry skin.
Reading: She is low in vitamins and minerals, especially zinc, and this causes the dry skin. She likely has a parasite in the lining of her colon, and for this reason the vitamins and minerals are not being processed throughout her body.

F 49 yrs 12-13-99
Problem: Skin cancer was removed from her leg.
Reading: Her skin is very sensitive to chemicals, and her blood is toxic. She needs to cleanse her blood and eat according to her blood type.

F 61 yrs 10-14-00
Problem: She has an itchy skin rash diagnosed as contact dermatitis. Dietary and laundry detergent changes have not helped.
Reading: The rash is not caused by her diet or by chemicals or toxins; her hormones cause it. (She then stated that the rash appeared after she had her hysterectomy.) Her hormones are very sensitive, and when she is tired or stressed her hormone levels are affected. Acupuncture would help her.

F 48 yrs 01-14-01
Problem: She has a history of skin cancer in four different body areas.
Reading: Her skin is chemically sensitive, perhaps to laundry detergent and pool chemicals. She should avoid alcohol and take selenium, which would help eliminate the free radicals from her skin.

M 62 yrs 02-19-01
Problem: He has rosacea, an adult reddish skin disorder. Medications are not working. He also has a tremor in his right hand.
Reading: He has an enlargement of the blood vessels in his brain that is allowing excess flow of blood, and this is causing the skin rash and trembling in his right hand. This swelling is a reaction to some form of toxic, chemical, or leafy poison type of plant.

F 41 yrs 07-02-01
Problem: For nearly a year she has had a breakout of reddish boils with puss, which has been diagnosed as folliculitis.
Reading: Her body does not tolerate dairy products, and this is affecting her circulation and clogging her pores, causing the skin boils. Eliminating dairy products is the most important approach to her health.

M 41 yrs 03-28-01

Problem: He has chronic facial acne for which he has tried many remedies to little effect. He also has red eyelids, which do not itch or burn but do increase in redness as the day goes on, and a light brown coating to his tongue that he can brush off but that returns again within a few hours. Two years ago he began having a vibration sensation in his entire body except for his head and neck. This occurs when he is at rest or beginning to fall asleep. A neurologist has not been able to find a cause.

Reading: An irregular neuron disorder in his brain in the area that controls sensory and visual processes seems to be the cause. This is triggering the vibration sensation and affecting the spleen and thyroid gland, which are the causes of the acne, tongue, and eyelid problems and have affected the blood. The neuron disorder appears to have been triggered by an electrical shock exposure of some kind between 9 and 12 years of age. (He then said that he shocked himself on his mother's electric blender when he was 10 years of age.)

M 44 yrs 04-15-01

Problem: He has acne and clogged pores. He is also losing his hair. Doctors at first believed that he had a hypothyroid condition, but tests have shown his thyroid gland to be normal.

Reading: His blood looks a little thick and shows high levels of nicotine, alcohol, and caffeine. He is not a smoker, but he is in a room full of smoke every day. (He states that he is a welder and is around exhaust all day long.) He is breathing these gases into his lungs, which is affecting his blood and the pores in his head. This is an environmental problem and is also causing the hair loss. He needs to wear a hat and better facemask when he is working around cars to protect himself from the exhaust, get more sunlight for his head, drink pure water, breathe purified air, and perform breathing exercises.

M 70 yrs 08-06-01

Problem: He developed a body itch 18 months ago that causes him to scratch so much that his skin bleeds. Topical lotions have not helped, although acupuncture did help somewhat. A test showing high blood protein suggests that he has kidney problems.

Reading: His kidneys are causing the itching because of a high uric acid content. He needs to flush his kidneys with liquids and take medications that would help counter the high levels of uric acid. Acupuncture would improve his kidney function 25% to 30%, but medication will help him the most. If he does not improve his kidney condition, his bladder may become toxic, poisoned by his urine.

M 70 yrs 10-14-01

Problem: His kidneys stopped functioning for 5 days 2 years ago and he was given only hours to live. He is now very weak, his skin is dry and itchy, and he wakes up tired. Doctors do not know why his kidneys failed.

Reading: His kidneys are lacking vitamins and are primarily responsible for his fatigue and weakness. He is also low in male hormones, which is the main cause of his dry skin and a contributing factor to his weakness. Perhaps his low hormone level also caused his kidney failure. Drinking apple cider vinegar would help his kidney function, and the potassium in the vinegar would help his skin and energy problems. His kidneys would also benefit from acupuncture and B vitamins in liquid form.

F 54 yrs 10-18-01

Problem: She has rosacea, a chronic skin condition. She has had much stress in her personal life.

Reading: Her pituitary gland is the cause of her rosacea. She should seek treatment for her pituitary gland to improve her skin problem.

SLEEP PROBLEMS

M 34 yrs 05-24-99
Problem: For most of his life he has slept only 3 to 5 hours each night. He also has nightmares and he sleepwalks. He wakes up sweating and hyperventilating and cannot determine if he is having a dream or if it is real. He also has anxiety attacks, which occur when he is extremely tired or when he is tired and trying to fall asleep.
Reading: He has a nerve dysfunction that separates his left brain from his right brain more than normal. He experienced head trauma at a very early age, possibly during childbirth. He needs reflexology to restore this nerve. Energy work would also open up his forehead and eliminate the anxiety attacks. Medication would not help.

F 51 yrs 10-19-98
Problem: For the past 5 years she has slept only 2 or 3 hours a night. She also has muscle spasms and back pain.
Reading: First, she needs to avoid caffeine because it is stimulating her pituitary gland. Second, she should relax her mind before bedtime. It might help her to read a book on self-relaxation. Third, she should see a chiropractor to work on her soft tissue and muscle spasms. This combination will help her sleep much better.

F 59 yrs 12-21-98
Problem: She has insomnia and digestive problems.
Reading: One reason for the insomnia is her digestive problem. However, she is not tired physically at bedtime. She needs to exercise at night.

M 46 yrs 11-03-99

Problem: He does not sleep well and wakes up tired. He loses his temper frequently.

Reading: His problem is a lack of exercise. He should work out in the mornings.

F 23 yrs 02-26-98

Problem: She does not sleep well at night.

Reading: When she goes to bed at night she is not physically tired, just emotionally tired. She should exercise in the evenings.

M 40 yrs 01-24-99

Problem: He suffers from a lack of sleep.

Reading: His lack of sleep is caused by "jump starting" his pituitary gland with sugar, caffeine, and chocolate. He should avoid these foods after noon. He also needs to see a naturopath for an herb that will restore his pituitary gland.

M 29 yrs 04-26-99

Problem: He has difficulty waking up.

Reading: He needs to learn relaxation techniques. His colon is inactive and needs roughage along with more water. Beer is affecting his digestion and his ability to relax. If he can mentally relax, eat better, and move foods through his colon more efficiently, he will spend less energy trying to wake up.

M 52 yrs 04-14-98

Problem: He has sleep apnea and has lost 85% of his hearing.

Reading: Weight gain, sugar use, allergy and sinus problems, and past smoking have caused a narrowing in the upper portion of his throat. This has brought on his early hearing loss and sleep disorder. He needs to sleep on his side, not on his back, to help the sleep apnea. If he does sleep on his back, he should elevate his head and shoulders. He might also try a natural throat lozenge or drink hot herbal tea with honey and lemon before bedtime.

F 43 yrs 02-21-99
Problem: She does not get enough sleep at night. She also has dull headaches and difficulty focusing.
Reading: The headaches, lack of focus, and sleep problem are all related to her low mineral level. She needs zinc, potassium, and other minerals in general. Sleeping longer will improve her concentration and focus.

F 41 yrs 11-01-01
Problem: She has had night sweats for the past 3 to 5 years and wakes up three to four times a night because of this problem. For the past 6 months she has been taking natural progesterone cream, which has helped her sleep better and sweat less. A test taken during her sleep has shown that her heart races.
Reading: Her hormone levels and heart look okay, but the problem appears to be her pancreas. It releases too much insulin at night while she is resting or sleeping. Contributing factors include stress, too much caffeine, not enough rest, and poor diet. She needs to improve her diet by increasing protein and decreasing caffeine, carbohydrates, and sugar. Breathing, relaxing, stretching, and managing stress are other important factors.

SMOKING/TOBACCO USE

M 59 yrs 07-01-97
Problem: He quit smoking 3 years ago and is concerned about his health
Reading: His palate narrows at the top more than it should, and the smoking probably caused this. He needs to monitor this problem.

F 44 yrs 10-11-99
Problem: She has low energy and has suffered from depression most of her life. She has been in therapy for the depression and takes an antidepressant, but nothing seems to help. She also cries easily and cannot take criticism.
Reading: Her low level of energy is caused by her depression, which was caused originally by loneliness as a small child. She needs to see a therapist who will help her cope with her loneliness. Smoking also contributes negatively to her depression.

F 46 yrs 05-08-00
Problem: She is frequently tired.
Reading: She is tired because of a lack of oxygen to the brain. The lower portion of her lungs looks 30% congested, probably from allergies, with cigarettes as a secondary cause.

M 20 yrs 02-09-97
Problem: He has chest congestion with a lot of phlegm.
Reading: His lungs are too congested for a 20 year old, and his smoking is a contributing factor to this problem.

M 47 yrs 04-19-00
Problem: He does not believe that he has symptoms or problems.
Reading: His bronchial tubes look irritated, although his lungs are okay. He has only about a 55% oxygen level in his blood. He needs to quit smoking because it is affecting his bronchial tubes and depleting the oxygen in his blood.

M 46 yrs 01-25-99
Problem: He has a dry, chronic cough. He uses one can of chewing tobacco per day.
Reading: The cough is linked to a sinus condition (60%) and to the nicotine in the tobacco (40%).

F 47 yrs 11-03-99
Problem: She has Graves' disease (a hyperthyroid condition).
Reading: Initially her thyroid gland acted up because of her smoking.

F 55 yrs 01-07-98
Problem: She has chest pains and says that she smokes too much.
Reading: The smoking has not had the negative health effects one would expect it to have on her. She should have more damage to her body than she does. Smoking probably will not even affect her to any major degree in the future, although it drains a large portion of her energy. Her throat and lungs look okay. This tightness in her chest is related to stress and fatigue more than to cigarettes. She does not eat well, nor does she eat enough throughout the day. She would rather smoke than eat. Food does not appeal to her, and she does not look forward to sitting down to a meal. Optimally she should cut down on her smoking and this would cause her to eat better than she does.

F 51 yrs 02-08-00
Problem: She suffers from depression.
Reading: Her smoking contributes to her depression.

F 54 yrs 02-05-01
Problem: She is depressed and very tired. She is a former smoker.
Reading: She is not medically depressed. She has an energy blockage to both sides of her neck, including the thymus gland. Her thymus gland has been affected by her smoking. Treating the thymus gland will also keep her from being so tired.

F 67 yrs 05-09-01
Problem: She lost a lot of weight during the past 3 years because doctors told her not to eat salt. Once she did, she was unable to gain any weight back. She has also had an aching pain in her neck, shoulders, and leg for the past 7 years. She smokes more than a pack of cigarettes a day.
Reading: Energy is blocked to her lower abdomen and reproductive area. Smoking is draining her energy and has affected her abdomen and hormonal level. Once this energy is opened, the hormones she is taking would be more beneficial. Her pancreas, low hormones, and low energy flow are causing the pain. She should drink apple cider vinegar to help cleanse the pancreas and decrease her craving for nicotine. Stimulating the thymus gland would also help reduce her smoking.

F 58 yrs 06-11-01
Problem: She has had osteoarthritis in her hips and spine for 7 years. Walking is painful, and she has muscle aches from the waist down.
Reading: Nicotine is irritating her blood. This in turn is bothering her upper lungs, the back of her head, and her spinal cord. She would benefit from acupuncture at the back of her head and neck and upper back, and she should quit smoking. Her thyroid gland was affected by smoking as well. (She said that doctors removed her thyroid gland 8 years ago, but she insists that she is only a light smoker.)

F 68 yrs 06-04-01
Problem: She has scoliosis for which she wears a back brace all day. Her back pain is worse when she is standing. Thirty years ago her pain

was in the upper back, but now it is in the lower back. Doctors do not know the cause. Three years ago she had heart attack symptoms and surgeons put a stent in her right ventricle.

Reading: Her cigarette smoking has caused toxins to form in her blood, and this is the key to her health issues for the past 30 years, including her lung dysfunction, digestive disorder, and heart and bladder problems. (She then stated that even though she did not mention it in the beginning of the reading, she has had colitis for years and has to wear panty liners because of bladder problems.). This is a chemical in her brand of cigarettes, but it is not the nicotine. She needs reflexology or acupuncture to the lungs, colon, and bladder and to quit smoking. Her adrenal glands are causing the cravings for smoking.

M 52 yrs 04-14-98

Problem: He is a former smoker. He also has sleep apnea and has lost 85% of his hearing.

Reading: Weight gain, sugar use, allergy and sinus problems, and past smoking have caused a narrowing in the upper portion of his throat. This has brought on the early hearing loss and sleep disorder. He needs to sleep on his side, not on his back, to help the sleep apnea. If he does sleep on his back, he needs to elevate his head and shoulders. He might also try a natural throat lozenge or drink hot herbal tea with honey and lemon before bedtime. To prevent further hearing loss, he needs to avoid sugar, dairy, and fats.

F 63 yrs 10-11-01

Problem: She was diagnosed with fibromyalgia and has had 8 years of chronic body pain. Her legs are her greatest problem—she can walk only a few steps at a time. She has a rare red blood cell (RBC) disorder that doctors believe is causing her leg problems. She is also very fatigued and unable to work because of her condition.

Reading: The lining of her lungs looks irregular, as though she were exposed to a chemical burn or smoke inhalation. This exposure has prevented her lungs from filtering blood properly and has resulted in her blood being poisoned. Blood passing through the digestive tract is not much better, and by the time it reaches her legs, it is in its worst condition with the RBCs nearly depleted. Her lung condition caused both the RBC disorder and the fibromyalgia. She needs to increase the oxygen level in her blood. (She then stated that she has been smoking since she was a little girl.)

F 61 yrs 10-13-01
Problem: She has back pain just below the shoulder blades that can move around to her front. She has had this pain for 6 years off and on, but it returned 3 months ago. Her pain is so intense that her doctors have her on a morphine drip.
Reading: Her lungs are causing this problem. Specifically, when blood leaves the lungs it passes through narrowed capillaries. (When asked whether she smokes she said that she does.) Smoking has damaged and narrowed her capillaries, and she is experiencing circulatory pain when blood and oxygen exit the lungs.

SPLEEN, PROBLEMS WITH THE

F 63 yrs 01-29-01
Problem: She has poor circulation in her legs.
Reading: She has too much fat in her blood, and this is causing not only gout but is affecting the spleen as well. The spleen is full of toxins and fat and is causing her circulatory problems. She needs almost all mineral supplements as well as energy work to the spleen, up through her chest, neck, and face.

F 43 yrs 03-04-01

Problem: She has had breast cancer in the right breast twice in the past 13 years. She now has a breast implant. Lately she has been experiencing pain under her left ribs with cold then searing, hot pain. Doctors believe it is a hiatal hernia with esophageal inflammation. She is taking acid suppression medication for it, and the pain has improved by 50%, but she still has bloating and cannot sleep well at night.

Reading: The breast cancer was caused by toxic blood, which in turn was caused by her spleen. In addition, her hormones have been imbalanced for 10 years, and this combination is behind the recurring breast cancer. The spleen is the cause of her bloating as well as her pain. She needs to have an x-ray examination of the spleen.

The most important thing she can do for her health and to avoid another cancer is to eat according to her blood type. The foods that she eats are incompatible with her blood type and the cause of her toxic blood. She should have energy work throughout her reproductive system, and after this is done she should have her hormone levels checked.

F 51 yrs 02-12-01

Problem: She has had chronically inflamed psoriasis for 10 years. The breakouts are on her buttocks, stomach, legs, and arms but not on her face. It is worse in the evenings and when she is under stress. She is being treated for it but with poor results.

Reading: The spleen is most likely the cause of the psoriasis. It looks clogged and fat engorged. Energy can be opened to the spleen with acupuncture and reflexology.

STRESS

F 25 yrs 06-14-99
Problem: She began feeling nauseated 2 years ago; 6 months ago her eyes became unequally dilated. Her breasts now lactate, and she has symptoms of pregnancy but is not pregnant. She is spotting between her menstrual periods. She takes an antidepressant for depression.
Reading: She is scared about life and what it will bring in the future, especially her job. Most of her pregnancy symptoms are stress-related. She has suffered from this emotional stress all her life because of the lack of love from her mother. Physical symptoms of stress began very early in her childhood, but she did not identify with them. She feels as though she is looking down at her body rather than being attached to it. She is very sensitive and can pick up on people's emotions very easily. She needs to share her emotions more freely. She does not have tumors or blood disorders, and her eye condition is emotionally caused. She needs to go back to the starting block and begin life anew. She should see a hypnotherapist who will take her back to her childhood and work on the emotions up through the years.

F 52 yrs 06-29-99
Problem: She was diagnosed with fibromyalgia. She becomes weak and often cannot get out of bed. Her energy level is low.
Reading: She does not have fibromyalgia. The stress in her life in 1993 took a physical toll that she is still getting over.

F 41 yrs 10-17-99
Problem: She has back, neck, shoulder, and lumbar discomfort. Her

appetite is poor, and tests by a naturopath have revealed problems with her liver, gallbladder, kidneys, and adrenal glands.

Reading: She has an energy blockage that is 2 inches above her navel and continues through the digestive organs, kidneys, and adrenals, up the back and base of the head, and down through the back of her neck into the trapezius muscles. Her adrenal glands are 70% exhausted. This energy blockage is stress-related. She cannot identify with it, so she does not know how to deal with it. Her issues are personal. Her husband should be included in the initial therapy to see if they can become closer. The order of treatment should be therapy for her emotions, energy work to clear the energy blockage, and acupuncture.

F 27 yrs 05-01-00

Problem: She was diagnosed with hyperthyroid condition. She gets the shakes and feels her heart beating too fast. Recently she has broken her engagement and has been told that she must get rid of her dogs.

Reading: Her occipital area looks off center, which is causing one side of her neck to pull at the base, twisting the muscles in the neck. The center and upper lobes of her thyroid gland are affected. The heart rate is connected to the thyroid condition, and both are linked to stress. Nothing is physically wrong with her heart; the heart rate is emotionally driven. The thyroid gland looks normal; it is just currently very active. If she works on her stress, her thyroid gland may return to normal. Acupuncture would help.

F 42 yrs 12-11-98

Problem: She has had heartburn since she started taking birth control pills. She wonders if it is connected.

Reading: The heartburn is very high in her stomach, mostly where the esophagus attaches to the stomach. This irritation can be dealt with by taking over-the-counter medications. It is partly caused by stress (70%) and partly by diet (30%). If she relaxes, breathes consciously, and regulates her medication and diet, the stomach problem will go away. The birth control pills do not cause the heartburn in the way that she thinks they do. The stress of worrying about taking the pill has increased her level of stomach acid and has caused the stomach irritation.

F 46 yrs 05-14-97

Problem: She has a lump in one breast that has been diagnosed as benign. However, she is worried because her mother died of breast cancer.

Reading: This lump has been very stressful for her. She has had a lot of stress in her life. She has activity in one breast, and it has inflammation. The lump is spreading, but very slowly. The other breast has a small, hard, nonactive lump. She is not handling her stress as well as she would like to believe. Stress is coming from her past as well as from an event that occurred between 1 1/2 and 3 years ago. She is also stressed because of current events from outside the home. She should ask doctors to monitor the tumor and avoid trying to fix it herself. Her efforts toward her mental state controlling the tumor have not been effective. She needs to work on the emotional side and quit worrying about the physical. Maybe later she can affect the physical, but she will need to be emotionally better than she is currently. She needs to go back to old hobbies that she used to enjoy.

F 50 yrs 07-09-00

Problem: She is beginning menopause and has low energy. Her job and schooling are stressful.

Reading: Her hormone level is just out of normal range. She has good health entering menopause, and a natural hormone will most likely help. She needs to learn to breathe and relax. St. John's Wort, communication with her husband, and hormone balance are factors in decreasing her stress level.

F 33 yrs 09-04-97

Problem: She is concerned about her complexion.

Reading: Nerves caused by stress are most likely causing her complexion to break out. She is on the go too much. She does not always need to be doing something. A slower pace would be good for her and is what she needs to heal her mind and body. She has a very active mind. She spends all day thinking too much about issues that are not important. She should read more to relax her mind and take it off unimportant issues.

F 57 yrs 10-06-98
Problem: She believes that she has a high level of stress.
Reading: Her stress level is not as high as she thinks it is. Her problem in dealing with her stress is finding a good tool to help her deal with it. She should go for long walks and learn to breathe consciously. She might even go back to yoga.

F 41 yrs 06-29-99
Problem: She is losing her hair.
Reading: Her hair loss is stress-related. She needs belly laughter; it has been a long time since she has laughed.

F 49 yrs 05-15-00
Problem: She had basal cell carcinomas (skin cancer) removed from her face, neck, and legs and is concerned about future growths.
Reading: The skin cancer is linked to vitamin and mineral loss, which in turn is related to her stress level.

F 40 yrs 04-14-01
Problem: She has pain in the lower back and hips, gallstones, an erratic menstrual cycle, and joint and leg aches. She worries that she might have cervical or uterine cancer. Her Pap smear has shown changes in her cells. She does not believe that doctors listen to her. They tell her to go home, keep a journal, and come back another time.
Reading: She does not have cancer, but she probably has rectal spasms, most likely from nerves. The problem appears to be a gland in the front of her brain. It surges high and then low, causing the reproductive pain. She has a fear of life, employers, and cancer. Her stress is so high that she can barely manage it. This stress has shut down her gland. (She then stated that her stress was so high at work that she quit and just

walked away.) She needs psychotherapy, relaxation tapes at night, yoga, and breathing exercises.

F 45 yrs 01-02-01
Problem: Her sex drive is low, and she believes that it is because of her hormones. She is being treated with herbs.
Reading: Stress is the problem, not her hormones. This began 5 to 7 years ago and has not been dealt with. (Her doctor then explained that her fiancé died 5 to 6 years earlier.) She should increase the herbs and try acupuncture.

F 74 yrs 07-09-01
Problem: Her muscles in her arms and wrists have begun to ache for the past few months, and she now has small lumps between the knuckle joints on the fingers of her left hand. She has also been very fatigued for the past 2 years, but she feels better after a nap. Doctors believe that she might have fibromyalgia.
Reading: She does have a light case of fibromyalgia brought on by stress, which has affected her adrenal glands and the lymphatic system in her chest and upper body. Stress is putting demands on the chemicals released from her brain, probably the endorphins, and this is causing the fatigue and muscle pain. She must learn to control the stress, which also can be treated with acupuncture. The adrenal glands can be treated with supplements and acupuncture. The lymphatic problem can be treated with massage to the arms, shoulders, and chest.

STROKES/TRANSISCHEMIC ATTACKS

F 69 yrs 02-26-01

Problem: She had a stroke last year that affected her right shoulder, hand, and arm. She is currently on a blood thinner and blood pressure medications.

Reading: She had a liver problem that lead to her stroke. She should have her liver tested and flushed with herbs. Walking and swinging her arms, cycling, and light weight lifting will all help her overcome the effects of the stroke.

F 55 yrs 07-01-01

Problem: She believes that she is having transischemic attacks, which are precursors to stroke. They last for 5 to 10 minutes, and she has a dull pain in her temple, loses all but peripheral vision, has numbness in her fingers, and has aphasia. She has a history of migraine headaches and is concerned because people with migraines are at greater risk for stroke than the general population.

Reading: Tension is causing a tight band that crosses over the temple and wraps around the mid-portion of her brain. This squeezing restricts blood flow to the brain and cuts off blood circulation, which in turn causes the dull pain to the temple, loss of vision, and numbness in her fingers. This occurs because her brain cannot communicate, particularly to the upper half of her body. Although symptoms would indicate a mini-stroke, this is not the proper diagnosis. It appears to be restriction of blood to the brain brought on by tension–the same reason for the migraines. She would benefit from cranial massage, relaxation, meditation every evening before sleep, and diaphragmatic breathing exercises. Meditation is better for her at the end of the day rather than at the beginning so that she can clear her mind of all stress before sleeping. She also needs to avoid caffeine, chocolate, and alcohol from noon on.

F 65 yrs 02-17-01
Problem: She had a hysterectomy and since then has had trouble with her hearing, vision, sleeping, and memory. Loud noises bother her, she is exhausted and confused, and she believes that her body is falling apart.
Reading: Her body is producing more scar tissue than it should, both in the sides of the neck and in the breasts. This results in a lack of blood and oxygen to the brain and puts her at risk for stroke. She needs a boost of hormones to prevent this scar tissue formation. Herbs for the brain would also help her thought processes.

SWALLOWING DIFFICULTIES

F 41 yrs 02-24-98
Problem: She has difficulty swallowing.
Reading: The difficulty in swallowing is caused by her esophagus being slightly off center. This can be adjusted by a chiropractor.

F 42 yrs 01-16-00
Problem: She has difficulty swallowing. An MRI revealed two small masses under her left jaw line.
Reading: The masses in her neck and throat are caused by long-term

energy blockage. If they are not treated, they will get worse. She needs acupuncture for the energy blockage.

M 60 yrs 02-18-01

Problem: He does not sleep well because his throat burns. He self medicates with an antacid.

Reading: His cranium is tight, and the top vertebrae in his neck are locked, pulling his head and neck backward. This is stretching his throat, particularly the upper throat and neck area, causing tightness of the tissues and creating the swallowing disorder. Rolfing would help free up the vertebrae, soft tissue, and cranium.

F 57 yrs 08-18-01

Problem: When she began menopause 4 years ago, she also developed pin-prick pains at the back of her tongue that have since moved to the left ear, down the left breast, and into the left arm. The pain usually flares up once a month, and she has difficulty swallowing. MRIs, barium swallows, ECGs, and thyroid checks have been negative.

Reading: She is having an allergic reaction. Now that her hormones have changed and she no longer has menstrual cycles, her body is more sensitive to airborne pollens. Perhaps she could have a test of her female hormone levels and then try to raise her hormone levels—not because her body requires the increased level but so that she will stop reacting to the allergens. Traditional hormone replacement therapy probably would be more effective than acupuncture and herbs.

TENDONITIS

F 52 yrs 12-13-98
Problem: She believes that she has arthritis in her hands; she is a massage therapist.
Reading: She may have some arthritis (her joints look inflamed), but most likely it is tendonitis, especially around the middle knuckles. Her shoulder ligaments are tight as well. She should drink apple cider vinegar for potassium, which will help these problems. Soaking her hands in the apple cider vinegar would also help the tendonitis.

F 65 yrs 12-06-98
Problem: Her right arm has been painful for the last few years. When she was young her arm would go to sleep. The pain is now on the top of the forearm and hand.
Reading: The arm pain is coming from deep in the shoulder, mainly from two areas: under the deltoid muscle and high up under the armpit. She has tendonitis and a lot of scar tissue. This tissue is cutting off the nerve and blood supply to the lower arm. She needs reflexology, acupuncture, and ultrasound. If this is not corrected, she could be facing surgery. This problem needs to be treated daily.

F 53 yrs 01-10-00
Problem: Her right shoulder started bothering her after having lifted something heavy 6 months ago. She has had 1 month of therapy, but it has not helped.
Reading: The right shoulder problem is a soft tissue injury, probably a strained tendon. It runs from the inside of the shoulder into the chest area. The injury has irritated the outside bursa sack as well. Acupunc-

ture would be the best form of treatment. Ice might help the bursa sack. She should also increase her potassium intake.

THYMUS GLAND PROBLEMS

M 38 yrs 11-30-98
Problem: He gets night chills frequently.
Reading: The night chills are a blood-pressure–related condition. His blood pressure drops while he is asleep, causing the chills. He needs to stimulate the thymus gland with a supplement to help control this problem.

F 54 yrs 02-05-01
Problem: She is depressed and very tired. She is a former smoker.
Reading: She is not medically depressed. She has an energy blockage to both sides of her neck, including the thymus gland. Her thymus gland has been affected by her smoking. Treating the thymus gland will also keep her from being so tired.

F 59 yrs 03-26-01
Problem: She was diagnosed with asthma 13 years ago and now has a chronic sinus problem. Steroids and antibiotics no longer seem to work. Four years ago she lost her sense of smell. She had polyps removed in her sinus cavity. Doctors believe that another polyp deep in her sinuses is blocking her ability to smell.
Reading: Her thymus gland is affecting her lymphatic system and her sinus passages. Her asthma is also connected to the thymus gland. Acupuncture to her thymus gland will help these problems and may even restore her sense of smell.

F 41 yrs 05-06-01

Problem: She has had health problems for the past 27 years. She does not know what is wrong, but she believes that it may be emotionally caused. She was diagnosed with Hodgkin's disease when she was 14 years of age. She was treated surgically and with radiation. Then she had to undergo a thyroidectomy because her thyroid gland was damaged by the radiation. Now she has left breast cancer, and her estrogen level is very high.

Reading: Her thymus gland is not holding energy. Energy enters the thymus gland and moves right through it and out the back of her neck. This is a result of her radiation treatment. It burned a hole in the gland. The hole in the gland needs to be closed with acupuncture and herbs, which should enable the body to hold onto its energy and come back into balance.

F 31 yrs 07-14-01

Problem: Fifteen years ago her throat began to burn, her face became hot and red, and she would nearly faint. This happened daily, although a full stomach would lessen the symptoms. Ten years ago her symptoms became much worse and she began eating more to minimize the symptoms. She can only sit up for short periods of time, and she faints if she moves her eyes or head. She also has diarrhea after eating and must eat hourly to avoid extreme acid burning in her stomach.

Reading: She has an energy block over her thymus gland, which is overly active, bright red, and causing her symptoms. Perhaps she had an infection of some kind that caused her thymus gland to react this way. It is possible that it is even cancerous. She needs to see a specialist to examine her thymus gland. This is a very serious condition.

THYROID GLAND PROBLEMS

F 59 yrs 09-27-99
Problem: She is being treated for a dysfunctional thyroid gland.
Reading: Acupuncture will help stimulate the thyroid gland and help improve her condition.

M 50 yrs 06-19-00
Problem: He has had low energy for 5 or 6 years. Recently he was diagnosed with a benign tumor on his thyroid gland.
Reading: His low energy is linked to his thyroid gland, which developed the tumor because of toxins in his blood. He needs energy work on his thyroid gland. He also might drink liquid vegetables to flush his organs and apple cider vinegar to flush his colon.

F 40 yrs 12-06-98
Problem: She was diagnosed with Graves' disease (hyperthyroid condition) 3 years ago. A recent thyroid test came back normal.
Reading: Her Graves' disease was triggered emotionally when she was in her mid-teens. (She then stated that both of her grandparents died when she was 14 years of age.) She has not dealt with these issues from her teen years, and she needs to do this so that her disease does not get worse or so that it can even improve. Seeing a psychotherapist would help her; once this is accomplished she can begin to heal. She also needs more time to herself so she can deal with her emotions.

F 27 yrs 05-01-00
Problem: She was diagnosed with a hyperthyroid condition. She gets the shakes and feels her heart beating too fast. Recently her engage-

ment was broken off, and she has been told that she must get rid of her dogs.

Reading: Her occipital area looks off center, which is causing one side of her neck to pull at the base, twisting the muscles in the neck. The center and upper lobes of her thyroid gland are affected. The rapid heart rate is connected to the thyroid gland, and both are linked to stress. Nothing is physically wrong with her heart. The thyroid gland looks normal; it is just currently very active. If she works on her stress, her thyroid gland may return to normal. Acupuncture would help.

F 45 yrs 01-31-99

Problem: She has cellulite.

Reading: Her thyroid gland kicks off and on rather than maintaining a balance throughout the day. Her hormones are affecting the thyroid gland, and this is anxiety-related. The thyroid gland is a factor in the increase of cellulite. She may need a year before she finds a hormone balance and starts to feel better.

F 47 yrs 07-11-98

Problem: She had her thyroid gland removed because doctors believed that it was cancerous (it was not) and since then has gained 100 pounds. She questions the type of thyroid replacement medication that she is currently taking.

Reading: She needs to change the thyroid medication. Her body is rejecting most of it, and therefore she is not getting the benefits.

F 39 yrs 10-04-99

Problem: She is overweight.

Reading: Her weight problem is thyroid-related. Her thyroid gland is okay, but it needs acupuncture to stimulate it. Other energy work would be beneficial as well, but acupuncture would be best.

F 54 yrs 08-20-00

Problem: She had a benign tumor of her thyroid gland removed and has nerve damage as a result. She wonders if she has multiple sclerosis (MS).

Reading: The thyroid tumor developed as a reaction to radiation exposure. Although most of her thyroid gland was removed, the remaining gland could still form more benign lumps. The remaining gland and the thymus gland need to be stimulated through reflexology. She also needs acupuncture for the pituitary and thyroid glands and homeopathic remedies for all of the involved glands.

F 55 yrs 02-01-99

Problem: She was told that she has thyroid problems.

Reading: Her thyroid gland is beginning to malfunction and needs energy work. This may be all the thyroid gland needs, but she might have waited too long. She should ask an older sibling if she was exposed to radiation or toxic chemicals when she was a child.

F 43 yrs 01-10-00

Problem: She has been told that she has a thyroid condition.

Reading: Her thyroid gland looks sensitive to fats and yeast. The outside lobes look the most irritated. Acupuncture of the thyroid gland would help.

F 47 yrs 11-03-99

Problem: She has Graves' disease (a hyperthyroid condition).

Reading: Smoking triggered her thyroid condition.

F 59 yrs 04-10-00

Problem: She is concerned about her thyroid gland; she is taking medication for it.

Reading: She should stay on the thyroid medication. Reflexology would help the thyroid gland as well.

F 53 yrs 12-29-99

Problem: Her heart beats very fast; she thinks it is caused by stress.

Reading: Her cardiovascular system looks good. She needs to have her thyroid gland examined.

F 25 yrs 04-03-00
Problem: She has extremely cold hands, for which she is taking thyroid medication.
Reading: Her thyroid gland can improve with acupuncture and reflexology.

TREMORS

M 62 yrs 02-19-01
Problem: He has a tremor in his right hand.
Reading: He has an enlargement of the blood vessels in the brain, allowing excess flow of blood, which is causing the trembling in his right hand. This swelling is a reaction to some form of toxic, chemical, or leafy poison type of plant.

M 50 yrs 07-07-01
Problem: He has tremors mainly in his head and hands. He believes they are hereditary because his mother has them as well. He is feeling run down.
Reading: His pituitary gland is the cause of his shaking. It is not functioning normally and is affecting his brain, which in turn is causing the tremors. Acupuncture and reflexology to this gland would be helpful.

TUMORS, BENIGN AND MALIGNANT

F 68 yrs 01-28-98

Problem: She has had a 5-year battle with cancer of the left breast. She is concerned about her liver and bones because cancer often spreads to these areas. For the last 6 months she has also been fighting an intestinal infection, which has caused diarrhea.

Reading: She has more dark streaks traveling from the left breast inward toward the center of the chest. She also has the same traveling outward and upward away from the left breast. This is most likely cancer, and the right breast also has two lumps. Cancer may already be in the bone (chest area). The current infection will not clear up in the near future. The white blood cells are off. The blood is too weak and too busy with its on-going cancer battle to fight this infection. She will need strong medication to fight this intestinal infection. She needs to get this infection under control because otherwise it will affect the body's battle with the cancer.

Cancer has not yet affected her liver, but it is not out of danger, nor are other surrounding organs and tissue. Her heart is strong and will remain this way throughout her ordeal. Her positive attitude has played a major role in her fight with cancer and can continue to do so. Therefore she must maintain a very positive attitude. Her mind is a very important element in her physical health, more so than in the average person. The old adage "mind over matter" is true in her current physical health and will continue to be so. She should seek alternative ways to encourage this type of thinking, such as tapes, books, or hypnosis.

F 50 yrs 05-20-99

Problem: In the past 2 weeks she has developed stomach pains and bloating. She thinks her stomach pain is a result of taking antibiotics. She believes that she has unfriendly bacteria in her digestive tract and is currently treating it with an herb.

Reading: The pain stems from the colon and moves from side to side. The bloating is caused by irritation and inflammation, not by a reaction to the antibiotic. She may have a fairly large blockage in the colon, most likely a malignant tumor. This blockage is causing severe inflammation and hence the bloating. She needs to see a gastric surgeon.

F 58 yrs 07-20-99

Problem: She has left side pain under the ribcage that comes across or under the breast. She belches a lot, which relieves the pain. She has had this pain for over 15 years. A naturopath is treating her with acupuncture, but she is not getting better.

Reading: She does not have stomach or colon problems. The problem likely stems from the adrenal gland over her left kidney. The kidney looks good, but it does have pressure on it. She has a tumor either on the adrenal gland or between the adrenal gland and the kidney. She needs to have blood and other diagnostic tests taken of this area.

F 53 yrs 03-23-00

Problem: She lost one breast to cancer 10 years ago and wants to know what caused the cancer.

Reading: Her breast cancer appears to have been caused by chemical exposure, stress, and energy blockage.

F 38 yrs 12-02-99

Problem: She was recently diagnosed with a benign breast lump; she also has gum problems.

Reading: The pituitary gland looks exhausted. This is a factor in the gum and breast problems. She needs to learn how to relax and meditate. This will help the pituitary gland.

F 60 yrs 03-03-98
Problem: She is concerned about a growth on her upper back. She has been told that it is a fatty tumor.
Reading: It would not hurt to have the fatty growth removed. This growth has tentacles and continues to spread out within the back muscles. It will continue to grow and become a nuisance and remain tender. The sooner it is removed, the less major the procedure to remove it will be.

M 66 yrs 04-22-98
Problem: He was diagnosed with cancer and given 2 months to live. Surgeons have removed a portion of his liver and want to operate again, but he does not want any more surgery.
Reading: He likely has more than 2 months to live and perhaps a chance to beat the cancer. He has energy blockage in his chest, which is why he is so physically tired. Doctors say it is because he is anemic, but his blood looks rich and healthy. The cancer is in the colon and is fast-growing, but it has not yet spread to the other organs. He should have another surgery; the doctors may get all the cancer. After the operation he can start reflexology, a change of diet, and getting his energy unblocked.

F 54 yrs 02-01-99
Problem: She had breast cancer 7 years earlier. She is on tamoxifen to reduce the estrogen response in her breast and hence decrease the risk of cancer recurrence. However, her naturopathic physician wants her to get off the drug because it is toxic to the body. Also, she has trouble breathing in the morning.
Reading: She needs to exercise. This is important for keeping her calcium and potassium levels up. Her sternum is sensitive because of earlier chemotherapy and is why it hurts to breath. She probably could cut back on tamoxifen, but she should not stop taking it. A mild, gentle cleansing of the blood and liver from the toxins left by the chemotherapy would be good, as would a little energy work on her stomach, liver, and sternum. Overall her health looks good.

F 39 yrs 10-08-99
Problem: She has liver cancer and has been told that she would have a 25% chance of living longer with chemotherapy. However, she refuses chemotherapy and is dealing with the cancer from an emotional standpoint. She has weekly colonic enemas.
Reading: The colon looks more cancerous than the liver. She needs chemotherapy, acupuncture, and herbs for the digestive system. She should increase her levels of enzymes and good bacteria and stop the weekly colonics. They are robbing her of her good bacteria. Her treatment needs to be aggressive, with 70% of it focusing on the physical.

F 62 yrs 02-26-00
Problem: She had cancer of the breast and a mastectomy a year ago. Medical doctors want her to have chemotherapy, radiation therapy, and tamoxifen, but she is determined to fight it the natural way. Currently a naturopathic physician is treating her with homeopathy.
Reading: She should follow the recommendations of the medical doctors. The homeopathic treatments are working very well, and she has no evidence of cancer, but it could spread to the sternum in the near future if she does not follow the more aggressive treatment.

F 49 yrs 05-15-00
Problem: She has had basal cell carcinomas (skin cancer) removed from her face, neck, and legs and is concerned about future growths.
Reading: The skin cancer is linked to vitamin and mineral loss, which in turn is related to her stress level.

F 45 yrs 10-30-00
Problem: Her left breast is painful, sore, hard to the touch, red, and flares up around the time of her menstrual periods. The breast improved after treatment with acupuncture, but then the pain returned with her period. Three years ago she had breast cancer and part of the breast was removed.
Reading: She needs an examination, mammogram, or ultrasound. She

has a small, malignant tumor just below and outside the nipple. This tumor is in the breast tissue, not the blood or bone. She also has an energy blockage from the pubic line upward through the digestive tract and up through the breast in a "V" shape. She needs energy work in that area.

F 43 yrs 03-04-01

Problem: She has had breast cancer in the right breast twice in the past 13 years. She now has a breast implant. Lately she has been experiencing pain under the left ribs with cold and then searing, hot pain. Doctors believe that it is a hiatal hernia with esophageal inflammation. She is taking acid suppression medication for it, and the pain has improved by 50%, but she still has bloating and cannot sleep well at night.

Reading: The breast cancer was caused by toxic blood, which in turn was caused by her spleen. In addition, her hormones have been imbalanced for 10 years, and this combination is behind the recurring breast cancer. The spleen is the cause of her bloating and her pain. She needs to have an x-ray examination of her spleen.

The most important thing she can do for her health and to avoid another cancer is to eat according to her blood type. The foods that she eats are incompatible with her blood type and the cause of her toxic blood. She should also have energy work through her reproductive system. After all this is done, she should have her hormone levels checked.

F 40 yrs 02-25-01

Problem: She was diagnosed 3 years ago with a benign pituitary gland tumor. Doctors decided to leave the tumor and treat her with medications. She is concerned because her family has a history of cancer.

Reading: She needs to stop drinking dark-colored carbonated soft drinks. These drinks have affected her pituitary gland and are the likely cause of the tumor. They have also affected the nerves that control her kidneys.

M 66 yrs 03-06-01
Problem: He was diagnosed with prostate cancer 3 years ago and underwent radiation treatments. He wants to know if they stopped the cancer. He has also been experiencing some rectal bleeding.
Reading: The prostate looks okay. He has a little bleeding in the rectum and colon caused by the radiation treatments, but this should heal in time. Diet would be important for this as well. He has an energy blockage in the colon, rectum, and prostate gland because of the radiation treatments. Acupuncture or reflexology to these areas would help correct this.

WATER RETENTION

F 39 yrs 10-04-99
Problem: She is overweight.
Reading: Salt is influencing her weight because she is retaining water.

M 62 yrs 09-28-99
Problem: He is depressed, bi-polar, and taking many strong medications for these problems. In the last 3 weeks he has gained 20 pounds, mostly water weight, and cannot put his shoes on because of the fluid buildup in his legs.
Reading: His main physical problem is his kidneys, which are the primary cause of the water retention. This is occurring because his medications are too strong. He needs St. John's Wort and other herbs, which would enable him to wean off his antidepressants. Acupuncture also would help the depression.

F 39 yrs 11-01-98
Problem: She is 65 pounds overweight. She has joint pain, and her digestive system and kidneys are a concern.
Reading: She craves salt and eats a lot of foods with sodium used as a preservative. She needs to eat more natural foods and avoid salt completely. She holds a lot of water weight, and the salt is also bothering her digestive system. She has a problem with her sweat glands, which are normal but slow to react, causing her to hold the salt. She also does not eat regular meals. Sometimes she eats twice a day, and sometimes she eats four times a day. She needs to plan meals and eat before she gets too hungry. She will have less joint pain when she reduces her salt intake. Also, her kidneys need flushing.

WEIGHT GAIN

F 41 yrs 07-20-99
Problem: She is very heavyset.
Reading: She needs to eliminate bread and yeast. Losing weight is a problem for her because of a strong emotional block. It started when she was between 9 and 12 years of age. (She then revealed that she was sexually molested around 8 years of age.)

F 50 yrs 07-19-98
Problem: She is overweight and has asthma and allergies.
Reading: Emotional and psychological problems are the main reason that she is overweight. She might try eating according to her blood type, but the best result will come from working on her emotional state. If she does not lose weight, it will start to cause a health problem. Her asthma and allergies also result from her emotions. The allergies

can be controlled through diet; the asthma will be helped through weight loss.

M 15 yrs 09-28-99

Problem: He weighs over twice what he should for his height. He dropped out of school at 10 years of age and has withdrawn from society. He does not want to live. He also has scoliosis and respiratory problems.

Reading: Losing weight would improve his life. He is not really depressed, to any level of concern, but he does feel sorry for himself. He is eating and gaining weight for attention, and they are his way of playing games with himself, his mother, and his doctors. If one were to tell him that his weight gain is a matter of life or death, he would not care; he does not value his life. He is bored and needs to discover something that he cares about so he can believe that his life has value. Once he believes that his life has value, one could approach him about the weight problem. Exercise and acupuncture could help improve his scoliosis, respiratory problems, and even his weight problem.

F 74 yrs 10-25-99

Problem: She weighs 300 pounds and wants to lose her excess weight. Her husband died 6 years ago, and she cannot accept his death.

Reading: Her emotional and physical states should be addressed at the same time. She needs counseling to help her move on from her husband in the physical world but stay devoted to him in the spiritual. Acupuncture would help her lose weight.

F 39 yrs 11-01-98

Problem: She is 65 pounds overweight.

Reading: She craves salt and eats a lot of foods with sodium used as a preservative. She needs to eat more natural foods and avoid salt completely. She also has a problem with her sweat glands, which are normal but slow to react, causing her to hold the salt. She does not eat regular meals and sometimes eats twice a day and sometimes four times a day. She needs to plan meals and eat before she gets too hungry.

F 59 yrs 01-25-99
Problem: She is having trouble losing weight.
Reading: Her weight really bothers her, but she has not had a reason to lose it until now (her age). She needs to focus on eating according to her blood type, avoiding breads especially. She can do this; she is strong willed and can accomplish great things if she wants to.

F 56 yrs 11-18-99
Problem: She is overweight and has had long-term sinus congestion.
Reading: The sinus congestion is mostly diet-related. Eating according to her blood type would help her sinuses and weight problem.

M 34 yrs 06-18-98
Problem: He is concerned about his weight.
Reading: Although his alcohol consumption is an emotional issue, his food consumption is not—he just enjoys it. He should eat according to his blood type. Emotionally he is ready to handle the weight loss now because he would be doing it for himself, not for others.

F 47 yrs 07-11-98
Problem: Her thyroid gland was removed because doctors believed that it was cancerous (it was not), and since then she has gained 100 pounds. She questions the type of thyroid replacement medication that she is currently taking.
Reading: She needs to change her medication. Her body is rejecting most of it, and therefore she is not getting the benefits. Her emotions will control and dictate her weight loss rather than her weight controlling her emotions.

F 42 yrs 02-29-99
Problem: She has gained 20 pounds in the past year.
Reading: Her weight gain is a result of a very slow metabolism. Energy

work and acupuncture would help. She should also use a treadmill to help her burn calories.

F 43 yrs 08-30-99
Problem: She has already been through menopause, is taking estrogen, and has gained 25 pounds. She wants to use herbs rather than the estrogen, but they have not worked.
Reading: She needs to stay with the estrogen, but it needs to be regulated carefully. She should take it every day at very low dosages, then increase the dose slowly over 5 to 6 months until she finds the proper balance. She will be surprised that her balance point will be very low. She can try herbs after she achieves the estrogen balance. However, her weight problem is 60% thyroid-related and 40% diet-related. She needs to stop eating breads and drink more water. The thyroid gland is sluggish and needs stimulation.

F 39 yrs 10-04-99
Problem: She is overweight and has a low sex drive.
Reading: Her weight problem is thyroid-related. Her thyroid gland is okay, but it needs acupuncture to stimulate it. Other energy work would help as well, but acupuncture would be best. Salt is also influencing her weight because she is retaining water. Her low sex drive is mostly physical—she is too heavy. She needs more protein, fewer carbohydrates, and more exercise. She also needs to drink more water.

F 25 yrs 04-03-00
Problem: She is concerned about her weight.
Reading: Red meat contributes to her weight gain.

F 54 yrs 05-29-00
Problem: She has gained 100 pounds.
Reading: She needs to cut out salt. Learning to breathe consciously will help her with her chocolate cravings.

F 54 yrs 02-05-01
Problem: She battles with her weight and wants to know if her weight problems are physical or emotional.
Reading: Her gallbladder is sluggish and is the reason for her weight problems.

F 41 yrs 07-02-01
Problem: She is tired and overweight (gained 80 pounds in the past year). She is also taking an antidepressant.
Reading: Her body does not tolerate dairy products, and this is contributing to her weight gain. Eliminating dairy products is the most important approach to her health. The antidepressant is not helping but rather is contributing to her fatigue and straining her liver. It is also slowing her digestive process and contributing to her weight gain. She should try a natural product instead.

F 36 yrs 06-04-01
Problem: She has been overweight all her adult life, which has gotten worse after three children. She has tried many diets and even has a personal trainer, but she still cannot lose weight. She only eats in the middle of the day.
Reading: Her energy is shut down throughout her entire digestive tract. Even her thymus gland is sluggish, which is why her metabolism is so slow. She needs to have her thymus gland stimulated and energy opened to her digestive tract, using acupuncture to accomplish both.

INDEX